MW00526273

A Five-Dimensional Model of the Universe

Michelle

Thank you for being
the good neighbor

Kennth

A Five-Dimensional Model of the Universe

A Quantum Theory

Kenneth L. LaPlante

A Five-Dimensional Model of the Universe:
A Quantum Theory

© Kenneth L. LaPlante
Copyright No. 1-TE512C
September 26, 2014

ISBN: 978-1-941066-43-0

Library of Congress Control Number: 2020911660

Book design by Jo-Anne Rosen

Wordrunner Press
Petaluma, California

If we can reconcile ourselves to the mysterious truth that the spirit is the life of the body seen from within, and the body the outward manifestation of the life of the spirit — the two being really one — then we can understand why the striving to transcend our present level of consciousness through acceptance of the unconscious must give the body its due, and why recognition of the body cannot tolerate a philosophy that denies it in the name of the spirit.

— C.G. Jung CW10:195

CONTENTS

PREFACE

The initial ideas and concepts that form the basic foundations for my models were germinating during my teenage years. I have been groping at the fringes of this new reality (ideas/concepts) for over sixty years. I have been both fascinated and repelled by the ideas and theories of a myriad of respected thinkers. I have been down dead-ends, dark alleys, despair, and revelations over this long period of time. On at least a half-dozen occasions, I just put the work aside. Whatever ideas were in me would die with me. However, my intuitive/abstract curiosity has somehow been sublimated into a personal journey toward understanding our empirical creation process and, by extension, the Creator.

My journey has taken on a life of its own. My two models — A Five-Dimensional Model of the Universe and The Creator — form the basis of my hypotheses. They represent my guideposts through which the process of expanding the scope of my individual papers has occurred: my attempt to delineate the structure of reality. Each paper has inspired the next piece of the puzzle to add "flesh" to the models. This book that I offer represents my progress to date. It is my journey to understanding the core of reality. It is a hypothetical quantum perspective built on the collected contributions from a thousand cognitive investigators across many philosophical, psychological, scientific, and religious disciplines.

I love the possibilities inherent in new ideas and concepts and feel the resonance of their magic in my soul. May it always be so. However, I have much work to do in my own process. I have my models and I have my path and I see glimpses beyond the curtain. Curiously, it seems to me that other observers do not recognize the curtain. In the words of C.G. Jung, "It is my peculiarity."

On an individual, personal basis, I must recognize those who have directly participated in and supported my work with so many acts of selfless energy and critical questions. The list must include Larry Partain, Ph.D. Physicist; Pastor Norman Theiss, Priest/Scholar Peter Kearney. Jungian Analyst Dr. Larry Staples kept me psychologically grounded from the easy ego traps.

The book would not have seen the light of day without the loving support of my wife Phyllis. She is my editor, counselor, and confidant — the true voice that never failed.

FOREWORD

Kenneth LaPlante, the author of *A Five-Dimensional Model of the Universe*, and I have worked together in advanced research and development and its support for over thirty years. In more than twenty of these years we were associates supporting such R&D at the Varian Central Research Center in Palo Alto, CA. Our work helped initiate the development of the first x-ray digital electronic flat panel imagers. Such panels have now almost totally replaced x-ray film in a way that has revolutionized and eventually dominated the field of medical x-ray imaging. For several of the earlier stages, our teamed assistance was able to help arrange for U.S. Government support that made such early stage, high risk, high payoff developments possible.

Kenneth LaPlante was trained as an engineer and has developed his concepts of Universe-level reality over a period of fifty years. He was inspired by the Nobel Prize winning activities of Planck, Einstein, Schrodinger, and others that directly led to the field of quantum mechanics which is quantified in empirical and physical terms. This extends well beyond the simpler and empirical space-time continuum of Newton.

This book attempts to explain the author's hypotheses of reality beyond the physical and empirical. It includes the concepts of spirituality and Creator which span fields of both physical and metaphysical reality. This approach considers the ever-increasing randomness or entropy of the evolving Universe. The book asserts that it is impossible to separate the physical and metaphysical aspects of the Universe which provide the basis of our evolutionary heritage.

Larry Partain, Ph.D.
Physicist,Solar Cell Electricity
Los Altos CA USA

INTRODUCTION

My three papers listed here* collectively form a new hypothesis on Universal reality. The first two papers hypothesize a model of our physical Universal reality in conjunction with a model of the Creator as a single entity (unity) comprising two fundamental components making up the Creator's "whole." The third paper attempts to consider the Creator's cognitive plan for our Universal reality (five-dimensional) based on the two hypothesized models. The combination of the three papers constitutes an outline of a new Universal reality — a skeleton of physical and meta-physical concepts abstracted and derived from the disciplines of philosophy, psychology, and religion (our cognitive trinity), along with those from empirical scientific study. The papers are offered as a guide to those of us with questions and issues about our present understanding of reality toward a new perspective in our relationship with the Universe and with our Creator. My three papers represent almost a life-time of abstract contemplation that began with studies of

---

* A Five-Dimensional Model of the Universe (copyright TXu 1-358-083);The Creator (copyright TXu 1-682-659); The Creator's Plan (copyright 1-7KAOEX).

Planck's experiments in 1900 on black bodies, through C.G. Jung's insights into the collective unconscious, and with J.S. Bell's theorem published in 1964. Dr. Bell's theorem gave me the impetus to write these papers since it provided the mathematical proof that, if the statistical predictions of quantum theory are correct, then many of our common sense ideas about subatomic phenomena and macroscopic events are profoundly mistaken. The statistical predictions of quantum theory have always been proven correct.

My recollection of an early enthusiasm for an expanded perspective on empirical reality was introduced by Einstein's special theory of relativity. The theory describes the relative aspects of physical reality (empirical) that vary under certain detectable input conditions. Physical reality relates time, velocity, and three-dimensional matter to their strict limits of functional operation in an empirical world. For instance, at the speed of light (empirical infinity), matter would be transformed into light.

However, the most startling scientific revelation that fostered my growing interest in a reality beyond our physical space-time model was Max Planck's experiments on "black bodies." These experiments ushered in a new scientific world of quantum physics. Our old models of elemental matter as "curious oscillators" were no longer representative as valid. They were replaced by Neils Bohr's atomic structure of the hydrogen atom. It is self-evident that without the experimental data from this new quantum perspective, my attempts to hypothesize the models for "A Fifth-Dimensional Model of the Universe" and "The Creator" would have been impossible. These two models represent both the physical and the metaphysical components of an eternal, single unity system that created our empircal world.

The empirical world we live in has already established scientifically that it was created, and that it is an entropic entity by nature. We live in a created world governed by immutable natural laws. For instance, the second law of thermodynamics usually refers to the idea that everything in our empirical world inexorably moves from a a state of order to disorder, and that entropy is the measure of that change (always increasing). Our empirical world is evolving toward a state of maximum entropy, resulting in its final temporal demise over a period of countless centuries of time. Entropy is fundamental to the pursuit of understanding a greater sense of reality beyond the empirical concept of a created world. Entropy is the *sine qua non* that underlies the validity of our empirical creation event, since it is not of itself eternal. Notably, an entropic system is capable of reproduction and cognitive interpretation, but it is not capable of creation.

Following the logic of a created, entropic system (our empirical world), it becomes imperative to investigate the creation process from an event that superseded our empirical world. We are fond of calling it the "Big Bang" theory. However, we are now in a quandary attempting to comprehend the reality of an eternal system — a creation event in conjunction with the idea of a Creator.

We could conceivably view the reality of our physical creation as a random, chaotic event. However, the idea of such a random event would logically negate the gifts of life and cognition to the living cell process itself. Also, a random event would deny the immutable natural laws that govern the Universe. There would be no sustainable energy system (no order) in the Universe and it would be devoid of existence. Whence comes energy?

There is no chaos in nature! There are powerful energy and cognitive forces that functionally operate to preserve and maintain not only our created empirical world but also the eternal system that energizes and governs the whole of reality.

BOOK ONE

Overview of Book One

The whole of the Universe cannot be described without theoretical models that are an integral unity of both physical and metaphysical components. Such models would constitute our perception of reality. In this sense, reality exists as a consequence of our perception of the nature of things.

My models of universal reality define and describe a unity concept. The models are functionally related and cannot be disjoined. They represent the whole of reality both physically and metaphysically. Together, they represent a five-dimensional system (both entropic and eternal) that operates and maintains a functional, universal reality. The models introduce us to a created entropic world and to the eternal system that created us.

The models briefly described here are offered as follows:

- A Five-Dimensional Model of the Universe
- The Creator

For simplicity, the book has been divided into Book One and Book Two, even though their collective contents represent a single hypothesis of a total unity reality. The parts are inseparable by nature.

Book One focuses on western empirical science that acquired its roots from the philosophical ideas of Aristotle.

Aristotle argued that the senses are the only sources of knowledge. This idea was adopted by the early scientific community for the purpose of experimentally investigating the myriad inquires/mysteries underlying the created empirical world. The mantra was that only repeatable experimental results were valid and useful to the community at large. Rationally, because of superstition and relative ignorance rampant in the middle ages, this sensate idea fostered an age of experimental discovery that propelled science to a level beyond its imaginings. This brilliant collection of scientific work is unparalleled in the human history of empirical observation and discipline. It introduced the classical physics models of temporal reality.

However, Aristotle was a man of his time. He was not burdened by the revelation of a quantum reality. He could not theorize that time is a relatively flexible, dimensional entity. He would not have been able to cope with the principle of complementarity. His logic and philosophical insight followed the course of evolutionary development during that historical period. As a consequence, he ushered in the era of the empirical attitude. Paradoxically, his empirical intuition was embraced by the scientific community and he became the father of our physical scientific world.

With apologies to Aristotle, the whole of reality cannot be described or understood in terms simply of a physical, entropic system. Empirical science has discovered an abundance of experimental data, particularly over the last hundred years, that has limited the old classical physics models of reality to a special empirical place in scientific exploration. Arguably, the key influence for this change in scientific thinking is the "black box" experiment by Max Planck in 1900. A new word

4

crept into the scientific literature that ushered in the idea of the quantum perspective. These ideas include the behavior of particles along with new models of atomic structure. These shifting realities present a difficult and complex process for our empirical scientific community to grapple with its troubling revelation.

Now the process has begun. We are beginning to introduce ideas into the literature that seem to extend our space-time physical reality. Examples include string theory which posits some fifteen dimensions, or another perspective which offers up to two hundred and fifty two dimensions without specifically identifying or characterizing any single dimension. These dimensional pronouncements may better be designated as perturbations or facets within our classical empirical model.

This book offers a hypothesis for the whole of universal reality, including our empirical world. As stated, the whole of reality cannot be defined in physical terms alone. New models must include the integration of a metaphysical entity into that sense of reality. This metaphysical world is a cognitive expression of our eternal natural laws.

The book begins with my modification of our classical physics model referred to as a space-time continuum. My model, *A Five-Dimensional Model of the Universe*, introduces a quantum perspective into this empirical sense of physical reality. The brilliant scientific contributions from Planck, Bell, Einstein, and many others have invited the world of science to proceed toward the new quantum world that awaits further investigation.

A Five-Dimensional Model of the Universe

Introduction

The four-dimension space-time continuum is the perfect model to describe Newtonian physical reality. However, the advent of quantum theory with its shattering description of sub-atomic particle behavior as a discontinuous process has limited the space-time model to a special case of universal reality.

The initial work of Planck, Heisenberg, Bohr, and others over the last one hundred years has ruptured the foundations of classic Newtonian physics.

However, it was not until Dr. J.S. Bell introduced his theorem of universal connectivity that I was finally encouraged to postulate a new physical reality model of the Universe. Bell's theorem mathematically proves that if the predictions of quantum physics are correct, then our understanding of the physical reality of the Universe is limited. The predictions of quantum physics have always been proven correct.

The Model for a Five-Dimensional Universe

My hypothesis is that the Universe is a five-dimensional mass/motion-matter/time continuum as contrasted to our general understanding of a four-dimensional space-time reality concept.

The fifth dimension is identified as that region beginning at the interface of the sub-atomic particle domain (at the interface barrier). The fifth dimension is characterized as that region containing all the mass in any functional universal five-dimensional system. The fifth dimension is a displacement phenomenon from our four-dimensional space-time continuum. The fifth dimension is displaced from our space-time continuum by the physical border that separates sub-particle phenomenon (mass) from cellular, organic particles (matter). These corresponding dimensional realities are inter-relational and provide the connected pathways for the functioning and the understanding of the Universe.

The five-dimensional mass/motion-matter/time continuum operates in accordance with the statistical predictions of quantum theory.

My five-dimensional model would then modify our present space-time continuum model to a massless, unified energy field. This unified energy field is expanding outwardly at a rate proportional to the mass content that generated it. This expanding space-time energy field provides our observed perception of universal reality. In contrast, the fifth dimension mass/motion region is expanding inwardly, in a reaction direction, at the same rate as the space-time energy field is expanding outwardly.

Matter does not exist in the fifth dimension. Matter (both organic and inorganic) is a four-dimensional manifestation of the mass particle content available from the fifth dimension. Matter is the resultant implicit derivation of fifth-dimensional mass into our four-dimension energy field. The four-dimensional energy field provides the receptacle/container through which mass particles from the fifth dimension are derived into matter. Matter defines our space-time perception (our sensors) of reality.

The model further implies that the mass particle content (fifth dimension) is the generator and the fuel provider that functionally operates our universal systems.

Motion is to mass as time is to our unified energy field (derived matter). Time is an indivisible space-time continuum concept that does not exist in the fifth dimension. Time is a special case of precise motion in the space-time model. Time is special in that it records the progress/history of any organic/inorganic operational universal system. Time records that activity in a forward, unidirectional progression.

Precise, constant mass particle motion is the fundamental, absolute requirement for the operation and regeneration of the Universe. Fifth dimension motion is a constant operational phenomenon that only indirectly relates to our concept of time. Motion is not a directional concept in my model. In the fifth dimension, a directional or forward concept of precise motion has no significance.

Comments on the Five-Dimensional Model

- The concept of the duality of light as wave or particle is consistent with energy waves (space-time) and mass particles (fifth dimension) reality.
- Light is fundamentally dependent on the mass/motion of particles. Light cannot exist without precise fifth dimension mass particle motion. Conversely, time is directly dependent on light. Time cannot exist without fifth dimension precise motion.
- Light is a constant, continuous mass/motion particle phenomenon. The model suggests that light is the complex

interaction of mass and energy operating in a functional "local" Universe. Light is always directly related to the precise motion of fifth dimension mass particle operation.

- The model hypothesizes that the expansion coefficient of the fifth dimension region is proportional to its total mass content. As a corollary, the extent of the expansion of the space-time energy field is proportional to the energy transfer from fifth dimension total mass content.

- The generally understood space-time concept of ether as an infinitely elastic, massless medium for the propagation of electromagnetic waves is hypothetically the same ether that propagates mass particles in a relativistically infinite fifth dimension.

- The model hypothesizes that the DNA/RNA complex molecular structure is the conduit through which our gifts of life and cognition have been derived and transported into the progressive generations of our species.

Example of the Model

The five-dimensional model implies that the Universe can be considered as a cluster of "localized" mass/motion-energy field units that are operational in their own individual time sequences.

Consider the phenomenon of the black hole in space. The five-dimensional model would theorize that the black hole condition was the result of a collapsing fifth dimension (highly compressed particle mass) in conjunction with a collapsing space-time energy field. The effect of this condition in a full collapsed state (potential condition of solid mass) would be devastating. Fifth dimension motion and its corresponding four-dimensional counterpart time would cease.

The condition of particle mass motion ceasing would create a collapsed mass/motion-energy situation that would be an absolute universal impossibility – and would be unsustainable. A condition of "expectant regeneration" would initiate an explosion proportional to the mass contained in the black hole.

At this moment of "expectant regeneration," constant motion would begin, and directional time begins to record the progress of this new "localized" Universe.

The fundamental requirement for the expectant regeneration of any black hole is the cessation of fifth dimension particle motion along with its relational time component. The black hole is primarily only a potential vehicle of regeneration.

The five-dimensional model simply hypothesizes a regenerative process based on localized mass centers. The model does not preclude the possibility that some single event occurred where all universal mass was located at a single node and the "big bang" resulted.

However, the five-dimensional model would require that the "big bang" was initiated by the fifth dimension, where no collapsing energy field or any space-time continuum entity could possibly have pre-existed. The "big bang" concept is an unlikely theoretical possibility in relation to the five-dimensional model, but it is primarily a complex conundrum.

Correspondence With Larry Staples, Ph.D., Jungian Analyst, on Five Dimensional Model of the Universe

Ken,

You deserve to have your remarkable document reviewed by people who can give you some really worthy feedback and appreciation. I do, however, have some intuitions about your ideas and concepts that I unfortunately have to filter and express through the template of a field I know somewhat better. When I read your piece, I have the feeling that in your discovery of the fifth dimension you may have entered along a scientific pathway the realm of God or whatever name we wish to apply to the creator and sustainer of all existence. Your paper states that the fifth dimension is the generator and fuel provider that functionally operates our universal systems. Your idea of a fifth dimension seems pretty close to religious conceptions of The Creator or God, and to the psychological concept of the self. All of these conceptions seem to me to convey the idea of some unseen unified source of all our energy and existence. In a way, I think you may have come upon a scientific explanation for what we are all looking for. It seems to me that there are many portals through which we can reach an understanding of what you have found scientifically in the fifth dimension. I don't, however, have the knowledge necessary to approach that realm through the scientific portal. I'm still trying to reach that realm by means I'm more familiar with.

It also seems to me intuitively that the fifth dimension may be the realm of the archetypes, in psychological and religious terms. You state that the four-dimensional energy field provides the receptacle/container through which mass particles from the fifth dimension are imaged into matter. The Bible speaks of our being an image of God and that God exists in an unseen realm that underlies and supports all existence. Jung speaks of the archetypes as the invisible source of images that shape both our psychic and physical existence in our four-dimensional lives. The source of these images could be the fifth dimension that you have well characterized in scientific terms.

Jung also said that will power is the amount of psychic energy that the self (the fifth dimension) makes available to the ego (the representative of the self that by necessity lives in the fourth dimension of space-time). In other words, our will power (expressed as psychic energy) is both supplied by and limited by the self. This idea of Jung seems intuitively to me to be connected to your statement that the extent of the expansion of the space-time energy field is proportional to the energy transfer from the fifth dimensional total mass content. Both you and Jung believe, I think, that the fifth dimension is the source of energy for our four-dimensional reality. In this construct, Jung's concept of the self would be similar to your concept of the fifth dimension. I certainly don't know enough science to assert any validity to this analogy. Nevertheless, I perceive it intuitively.

I do think I remember vaguely from the distant past a couple of scientific ideas that may be related to what you are saying. However, I'm not at all sure. Whatever God is —a word, a thought, pure reason, pure energy, a cell, a particle, a wave, a string, a tendency toward natural selection — he/she/it appears to be, paradoxically, the greatest power derived from the smallest size. This phenomenon is implied in the finding that the nucleus of an atom is one-millionth its volume but 99.9% of its mass. I think I also remember that scientists assume that the radius of an electron is zero, but don't know why a particle can have no size and structure and yet have a mass. I'm wondering if mass in these last two statements comes from your fifth dimension?

Larry

Larry,

Thank you for reading my paper and your kind and supportive comments regarding my intuitive/abstract ideas.

It is just synchronistic that your intuitive thoughts seem to connect the Creator to the fifth dimension. I have started writing my second paper (my plan is to write a total of three) on the subject of the Creator. It has been my intention for some months to connect the fifth dimension to a concept of God (as you say the "sustenance of all existence"). Your thoughts encourage me to push into this realm.

The problem with the assumption that the radius of an electron is zero is that — since the electron is a sub-atomic particle (a fifth-dimensional phenomenon) — its physical properties can only be inferred by experimental reference. The sub-atomic particle world (fifth dimension) is only presently available to us as statistical predictions (always correct) from quantum physics experiments.

My model hypothesizes that Bohr's model of the atom is essentially correct. His model does not have to be correct to support the fundamental premise of the fifth dimension — it just makes it more convenient.

I love your comment that the greatest power is paradoxically derived from the smallest size. I see mass/motion as the essence of our whole Universe. The inherent, unchanging nature of our universal process and evolution. Philosophically, that essence may only be found by looking into the character of the seed from whence it all began.

Kenneth

The Advent of Our Space-Time Continuum:

A New Perspective on the Big Bang Theory

Introduction

The prevailing cosmological model of the early development of the Universe is the Big Bang theory. A simplified version of the theory was proposed by George LeMaitre in 1927. Many contributors including Einstein, Friedman, and Hubble offered further insights into the implications of this theoretical concept. However, the creation of the Universe is not understood and is still an area of open investigation. Fundamentally, the Big Bang theory does not provide any information for the initial conditions present at the inception of the Universe, but rather it attempts to describe and explain the general evolution of an expanding space-time continuum going forward from that event. The basic principle of the Big Bang is that the Universe is expanding. Unfortunately, this important observation has somehow led to a general view that the Big Bang was the advent of the Universe.

The primary question of any Universal reality is whether any part or any aspect of that reality is eternal. If not, then the issue of eternal reality must include the prospect of a Universal void. (See my paper, "The Void Concept.") My theoretical conclusion from that paper is that the Creator of the Universe is an eternal concept. Further, that the empirical reality we call our space-time continuum was created from a plan and purpose by the Creator.

Two Universal Events

The Big Bang theory is potentially an expansive and complex idea that has been speculated upon and represented as a single, simplified, explosive image of the creation process. This paper represents an attempt to further understand the complexity of the creation process in terms of two separate and creatively distinct Universal events.

First is the advent of our space-time continuum. Space-time is not an eternal concept. It is an entropic entity and it was created by an action instigated by the eternal Creator as pat of a purposeful intent and plan.

The second space-time event is the re-generation of temporal sectors (solar systems, galaxies) that are necessary to perpetuate space-time. This re-generation process requires energy from space-time in conjunction with the energy forces latent in mass-motion (fifth dimensional entities). My hypothesis contends that the combination of these energy forces is theoretically sufficient to instigate the process of space-time "sector" re-generation. This process always operates in accord with Universal, natural laws.

Connecting these two Universal events, the validity for the creation of space-time is supported by the laws of thermodynamics. In that context, space-time must be a system capable of re-generation or must suffer its own demise. The Big Bang theory has, over the years, implied a "creation" concept to space-time, but science has been tacitly unresponsive to the quandary of attempting an explanation of "creation" in terms of an empirical idea of reality.

The creation of our space-time continuum cannot be described or understood in relation to an empirical model of reality for two reasons:

First, space-time is incapable of its own creation. It is not an eternal concept. It is an entropic system in a state of constant decay. However, it does have a specific role in the re-generation of Universal sectors (solar systems, galaxies) in our space-time Universe.

Second, the space-time model does not give credence to the function or role of the natural laws in the operation and governance of the "Whole Universe." When these natural laws (thermodynamics, calculus, etc.) are a part of the creation question, they are generally described in terms related to a quasi-physical reality. Theoretically, natural laws are to be understood as eternal, metaphysical entities that operate and govern the whole of the Universe as part of the creation process. The idea that creation can be defined in physical terms alone is rife with riddles and dilemmas and in need of a new perspective.

First Event — Initial Conditions for the Advent of Space-Time

As stated, the creation of space-time is impossible to describe in an empirical sense of reality. The apparent assumption of the space-time model is that matter has hypothetically existed (was not created) and that matter and mass are basically the same entity and operate in the same dimension. In this context, our empirical concept of reality tacitly implies that space-time was not created, but is eternal. However, the laws of thermodynamics are unassailable in regard to space-time being entropic. Space-time is a temporal entity in constant decay.

At this point, it is imperative to introduce a dimension beyond space-time. A fifth-dimensional model of reality that theoretically expands space-time to a new concept of mass/motion - space/time, where mass/motion are eternal fifth-dimensional entities, and where space/time are implicit derivations from these fifth-dimensional entities. While mass and matter are directly related physical entities, their functions and operations in the whole of the Universe are differentiated by the nature of the creation process.

The initial conditions for the advent of space-time are by necessity eternal concepts. These concepts reside in the fifth dimension, and they are mass and motion. They represent the physical engine of the "whole" of the Universe. Operating in conjunction with these physical entities are the Universal natural laws that provide the operation ad governance functions for the creation process. (See my papers, "A Fifth Dimensional Model of the Universe" and "The Creator.") My models hypothesize that the creation of space-time would logically follow from a process of Universal natural laws operating in conjunction with the energy engine (mass-motion) of the Universe. The catalyst for the advent of our space-time creation is the eternal calculus through a process of an implicit derivative operation from the fifth dimension.

Second Event — Re-Generation of Space-Time

My expanded fifth-dimensional model of a mass-motion, space-time concept of reality introduces a new perspective to the idea of localized re-generation of solar systems/galaxies within the whole of the Universe.

A potential vehicle for localized, space-time re-generation is the black hole phenomenon. Assuming that certain Universal (five-dimensional) operating conditions are activated, a black hole is hypothetically capable of reproducing a new star system. In the death throes of a black hole, space-time and mass-motion are collapsing upon each other in opposite, contracting directions toward a singular focus point. The energy from these collapsing forces is theoretically attempting to create a Universal solid. These opposing forces could potentially confront a situation where motion would cease. However, motion is an absolute, Universal constant. The absence of motion is a Universal impossibility. The result of such a static condition would be cataclysmic. The process of localized space-time generation would be initiated.

Comments on the Big Bang Theory

As stated, the Big Bang theory does not consider or attempt to explore the initial conditions for the advent of the Universe itself. Its primary theoretical principle is that the Universe is expanding. On this basis, the theory cannot purport to understand the creation process of our space-time continuum. In a narrower sense, the theory seems to attempt an understanding of a process of a localized re-generation phenomenon within space-time itself.

Space-time is a collection of energy centers (galaxies and solar systems) that operate as an interconnected, interdependent whole. These energy centers operate as temporal units in conjunction with natural laws. The lifetime of these energy centers varies in time and intensity determined by their energy quotients. Their re-generative processes are hypothetically instigated by the phenomena of dying stars (black holes).

My hypothesis interprets the re-generation of a localized energy center (black hole) as being incapable of activation by the forces available in space-time alone. The energy engine of the whole Universe (mass-motion) must operate in conjunction with these forces to provide the spectacular energy necessary to collapse a black hole into a "near solid." Again, such a condition would instigate a space-time cataclysmic event.

Conclusion

The supposition that the advent of our space-time continuum was the result of a single eruptive event at a single point in the Universe is speculative. The creation process could just as likely have been a series of Universal "sector" related events. In either case, the creation process (the advent) represents the birth of space-time into the whole of the Universe. This creation was not a random event. It was part of the Creator's plan. Concordantly, there is no chaos in the nature of things. The "whole" of the Universe is not a chaotic system. It operates through a network of natural laws that govern the inter-connectability of an orderly system.

The creation of space-time is, by nature, followed by a process of re-generation. This re-generation process is a necessary consequence of the nature of space-time being in a state of constant decay.

Correspondence with Larry Partain, Ph.D., Physicist, on Big Bang Theory

Ken,

As usual, I find your writing quite fascinating and stimulating. You quite shrewdly observed that the big bang theory has absolutely nothing to say about initial conditions. You also note the confounding problem of the conservation of mass and energy with time. Reasoning from that, the initial conditions cannot have been nothing. However, I have struggled to incorporate all this with your prior ideas of spirituality being the fifth dimension. I am not sure I am ready to have this set aside so that mass-energy can now be the fifth dimension, unless one speculates the latter is the primary attribute of the fundamental "Creator." I need to think a lot more about your latest ideas.

Larry

Larry,

Thank you for reading my paper and for your comments.

My Creator model is hypothesized as a single unity comprising two fundamental components.

A physical component which provides the "energy engine" for the Universe. This energy component comprises mass and motion.

A metaphysical component which provides for the operation and governance of the Universe through the immutable natural laws that sustain its existence.

Both of these physical and metaphysical entities are eternal and reside in the fifth dimension. They make up the Creator's whole. My next paper is entitled "The Nature of the Creator" and will attempt to expand my ideas on the metaphysical components of the Creator's nature.

Kenneth

A Quantum Perspective on Black Holes

Introduction

The recent news of the Laser Interferometer Gravitational-Wave Observatory (LIGO) experiment that proved the existence of gravitational waves in the fabric of our Universal aether provides an opportunity to study and map black holes. Gravitational waves are a natural Universal phenomenon and will be a useful tool in exploring the complex operational functions of the black hole in our space-time continuum. Our present empirical attempts at understanding the process and purpose of black holes have produced extraordinarily important results, but Universal mysteries remain that are compromised by the limitations of classical physics.

Much of the present understanding of black holes are simulation models based on extrapolated data from several sources, including the Hubble telescope, the Michelson/Morley interferometer, and other empirical methods of investigation.

A problem is that the functional operation of black holes is not completely available to us in an empirical model of reality. Black holes are not entities that can be fully understood by the practical application of sensate methods. In that respect, they are complex invisible entities whose function is to provide for Universal sector re-generation in our entropic space-time continuum system.

The Black Hole as Interpreted in Our Space-Time Model of Reality

The scientific literature on black holes is presented to us by data from the Hubble telescope, which offers useful information from past cataclysmic events in the Universe. This information is communicated to us at the speed of light following the event. The nature of black holes has also utilized important ideas like the Michelson/Morley interferometer tool and the Bekenstein/Hawking radiation emission hypothesis. The black hole is understood as an invisible entity on the basis that light is unable to be radiated or emitted from its core. In that perspective, we are not able to see black holes. Rather, we speculate about the presence of Universally localized, dying super-novas capable of re-generation in our space-time system. The speculation about this localized re-generation process has led us to offer an empirical hypothesis for its efficacy.

Our present understanding of black holes from a classical physics model includes the phenomenon of dying stars, but not just any star. Black holes require a massive star or stars. For instance, our sun is not in the massive category. The scientific expectation is that it will swell up into a red giant (in a few billion years) before it cools to a white dwarf. It will not regenerate but rather it will die in a spectacularly brilliant death.

Conversely, when a massive star dies, the remnant core can be so dense that it creates a black hole. At this point, the scientific literature becomes somewhat vague. However, a massive star that explodes (went super-nova) creates super-nova remnants blasting bits and pieces of the massive star (their chemical creations) into space. The effect of that is to seed the localized Universe for a new generation of stars. When a massive star explodes into a super-nova, the central part of the star collapses under gravity, creating a neutron. When the neutron rotates rapidly, it is called a pulser. This action develops high-energy particles in the super-nova that are dispersed into space. Presumably, the pulser is the instigator of the re-generation process.

Another question compounding our understanding of the black hole is related to the black hole "boundary" area increasing (never decreasing) if all of its localized boundary matter is captured within that sector's influence. Under this condition, the laws of thermodynamics would require the black holes to give off radiation, suggesting that its boundary surface (matter) is its entropic contribution to Universal sector re-generation. However, the fundamental question is how are these physical (matter) boundary surface actions impacting the whole operational process taking place in the core of the black hole. The black hole is not a stand-alone entropic concept. Without consideration of Universal quantum effects and functions, the understanding of the complex process of black hole re-generation will continue to be wrapped in an invisible conundrum.

This paper attempts to connect these important empirical ideas on black holes with a quantum-based hypothetical perspective to understand the relationship of our entropic (space-time) system with the eternal operating system in the whole Universe.

A Five-Dimensional Perspective on Black Holes

Since the advent of the quantum discovery by Max Planck in 1900, a new quantum model has been required to explain our complex Universal reality beyond our created space-time system. The classical model is limited in scope to interpret certain scientific discoveries related to our quantum Universe. Science requires a model of quantum reality to mold new discoveries into the present classical picture of reality. A reality that encompasses our empirical model expanded to integrate the complex forces of our natural laws (their metaphysical nature) and the relationship between entropic and eternal operating systems in the whole of the Universe.

Unfortunately, our empirical perspective has resulted in certain scientific discoveries being interpreted as confusing and misunderstood. Examples are Heisenberg's brilliant interpretation of uncertainty (See my paper "A Quantum Perspective on Heisenberg's Uncertainty Principle"), along with the black hole phenomenon as perceived through the prism of classical physics.

A hypothetical approach to understanding the complexity of black holes from a quantum perspective is offered as follows (See my paper "A Five-Dimensional Model of the Universe"). For purposes of discussion on the subject matter the following ideas are pertinent:

- My model expands the classical space-time model to a mass-motion, space-time concept.
- Mass-motion are the fundamental building blocks of the whole physical Universal operating system. They are eternal realities.

- Matter-time are created, temporal entities derived from mass-motion.
- Mass and matter are not the same entity. While they are intimately related, their function and operation in the Universe are dimensionally separate and distinct.

In our classical model of reality, the black hole is described as a non-emitting, invisible entity in space. In that model, it will always be a mysterious and misunderstood concept. We will continue to witness its effects from a past cataclysmic event. It potentially becomes a "hole" or a "rupture" in the fabric of space. What could that conceivably mean in a classical space-time continuum model except as an eternal mystery.

My hypothetical quantum model would analyze the black hole phenomenon from a mass-motion, space-time perspective where mass-motion are eternal entities that reside in the fifth dimension and where matter-time is our created, entropic system.

At this point, it is important to repeat that space-time as described in the literature is an entropic system. More completely, it is a thermodynamic entropic system. Entropy is defined as a measure of thermal energy per unit of temperature that is not available for useful work. An entropic system progresses in the direction of increasing entropy. The consequences of this directive action are:

- The prohibition of perpetual motion systems.
- The arrow of entropy is the same as time.

In an isolated system (natural) entropy never decreases. The system spontaneously evolves towards thermodynamic equilibrium to the state of maximum entropy — an ultimate matter and energy state of inert uniformity.

The second law of thermodynamics states that the total entropy of any system will not decrease other than by increasingly the entropy of some other system. In effect, space-time is a naturally inefficient operating system that began its decay at its inception. By definition, space-time is a temporal system and cannot perpetuate a propagation of Universal sector re-generation. Space-time must operate in conjunction with an eternal system, the same eternal system that created our entropic, space-time system.

Seeking answers to Universal sector re-generation using classical models will be complicated by using entities like mysterious, invisible black holes to describe the natural process of re-generation, unless we recognize the efficacy of an eternal system. Black holes certainly exist in our Universe, but they cannot be interpreted or understood under the terms of an entropic system alone.

A black hole is the vehicle for sector re-generation in the Universe. The black hole could theoretically provide an opportunity to understand the interaction and transfer of energy from an eternal state (fifth dimension) to its created derivative state (space-time). In this five-dimensional sense, the complex process of sector re-generation could be understood in terms of the natural laws that govern and perpetuate the whole of the Universe.

The black hole provides the key to understanding the physical and metaphysical underpinnings of the nature of Universal reality. As matter was derived from mass in the creation of our space-time continuum, this special event of sector re-generation represents a singular opportunity where the eternal physical operating system (mass-motion) operates to perpetuate a dying entropic system (black hole) by employing a dimensional state transfer or, in mathematical terms, an operational derivative transfer into a newly reseeded super-nova entity.

My fifth-dimensional model would hypothesize that forces acting on the massive star/stars are not only gravitational but also dimensionally related and are functionally active and pervasive. The mass of the dying star is waning (collapsing) under gravitational forces emanating from the fifth dimension. In conjunction with this action, all of the matter available in the localized region is being squeezed by space-time gravitational forces in an equal and opposite direction. In effect, the natural forces of mass and matter are imploding upon each other. The result is the creation of a localized black hole. This black hole entity is inexorably being squeezed into an untenable Universal condition as it approaches an absolute solid. My model hypothesizes that, while time is a temporal derivative of motion, motion is an absolute Universal constant. A mass solid is an unsustainable condition in any sense of reality. In this case, the resultant implosion would be a cataclysmic event which would usher in a new localized super-nova that regenerates our sector, space-time Universe.

My model envisions the black hole as a complex, non-isolated system. Its operational process functions to provide a decrease in thermodynamic entropy by providing the necessary mass energy (the quantum quotient) from the eternal system to the dying star, functionally activating this entropic system that will effectuate the resulting new super-nova reseeding process.

Conclusion

The extraordinary contributions of the scientific community toward an understanding of the complex phenomenon of the black hole cannot be underestimated. Without their research data, hypotheses, and observations on empirical reality, it would be impossible to explore the regions and the behavioral activities of our quantum Universe.

The black hole provides us with a unique and extraordinary opportunity to study and understand the complex operations and functions between our entropic and eternal systems. As understood, the black hole process operates to re-generate (reseed) our space-time system on a Universal sector basis. This process is quite different from the initial creation of space-time usually referred to as the "big bang." They are separate and distinct events. (See my paper "The Advent of Our Space-Time Continuum," copyright 1-TE512C).

My idea that Universal sector re-generation is being actualized by the application of eternalmass energy into a dying matter entity (decreasing entropy) would suggest that a purposeful creation plan has been activated (both physically and metaphysically) to rejuvenate an entropic system (space-time) on a sector basis. The operation of our immutable natural laws in conjunction with mass energy transfer argues emphatically against a proposition for the idea of random events in the Universe. The creation of space-time along with its sector re-generation is the primary element of the Creator's plan for the Universe.

Letter on Black Holes from Larry Partain, Ph.D., Physicist, Translational Research Associates

Ken,

I just read your latest blog paper on a quantum perspective of black holes. The first thing I liked about it is that it is very readable unlike most other attempts I have seen trying to reconcile quantum mechanics with the physics of that of massive "large" including black holes. The second is the observation is that no one knows much about black holes so that your speculations about them could be just as "true" essentially as any other. Your comprehension that gravity waves are an important tool since these presumably came from the collision to two black holes. They beg the question of what happens to gravity waves as they pass very near black holes. Will that give us relevant tools to observe and learn what gravity waves and black holes are all about? You mention that entropy is a universal metric that never decreases in a closed or compete system but somehow our Universe has not degraded into the complete chaos the maximum entropy would require. Somehow some kind of "local" regeneration occurs. Your suggestion is that some of the explanation may lie in a fifth dimension. As I think of dark matter and dark energy that are also totally unexplained I wonder if it might be some of the mass of multiple other galaxies that are only detectable through dark matter and dark energy (from a fifth dimension) that presumably should interact someway with black holes and gravity.

The only weakness I found is that it describes no experiment that could falsify or confirm this fith-dimensional explanation. However this is not a harsh weakness since there are really no relevant theories that could also be so "tested" in a scientific manner. This includes "string theory" that remains a "philosophy" in that it identifies no specific experiments that could be scientifically "falsify" or "confirm" its concepts. Overall a very interesting read.

Larry

Correspondence on Black holes with Larry Staples, Ph.D., Jungian Analyst

Ken,

I've read your very interesting paper on black holes. While my understanding, as with all your papers, is limited by my own lack of sophisticated knowledge of the scientific concepts that you easily grasp and navigate, I do arrive at a kind of primitive intuition about them. And from past readings, as well as the reading of this one, I sense that the very complex concepts and constructs that you express on paper are a reflection of deep insights that exist inside your psyche and see into eternal natural laws that govern the operation of the complex universal reality beyond our created space-time system.

My layman's understanding of what I believe you are saying is basically that the system that created all that can be seen and measured now was created in the beginning by factors lying in the fifth dimension that cannot be seen or measured. Despite all the amazing empirical advances in measurement, the system that accounted for the initial creation as well as the regeneration of that which dies out, cannot be seen or measured. It is the universal mystery. The visible system eventually degenerates and disappears.

The system that created the visible one never disappears, but keeps regenerating. I gather you believe it is the fifth dimenson that will reseed the black holes and by very complex operations bring them back to life. Would it be proper to say that a black hole could serve as the womb into which new seeds of life are planted by the operation of creative forces in the fifth dimension?

Larry

Larry,

Thank you for reading my latest paper on black holes and your comment on the material.

Your primitive intuition (your words) would mirror my perspective about eternal natural laws.

The created entropic system (space-time) is dimensionally and functionally separate (it was derived) from the eternal fifth dimension. The two systems represent the whole of the Universe and its functional reality. The complex functions of the eternal system (mass-motion along with the natural laws) operate to maintain and perpetuate the whole of the Universe (all five dimensions), while the entropic space-time system operates to the limits of its created function. Specifically, the black hole condition of being invisible is directly related to the extraordinary forces being applied to the dying star/stars, to the extent that in this collapsing condition, light is turned inward and cannot escape the region of its influence.

Our space-time sensate functions cannot visualize the black hole. This empirical condition does not suggest that factors in the fifth dimension cannot be measured. They can be measured, as they are intimately related to their created entropic system if they are understood in terms of a quantum related model of reality.

Yes, the black hole could serve as a womb for the new seeds of life — lovely poetic expression.

Kenneth

A Quantum Perspective on Heisenberg's Uncertainty Principle

Introduction

The discovery of the quanta (Planck's black box experiments in 1900) has led science down new and unknown paths toward recognizing peculiar uncertainties in the sub-atomic realm, for example:

- Bohr's idea of complementarity, describing something that can be a particle or wave at the same time, but must always be measured to be one or the other in any particular experiment.
- The energy of a photon (a massless wave) and its apparent peculiar behavior in relation to a wave or particle is known in classical physics by applying Maxwell's equations (Schrodinger's analogue) to give a law of motion for a photon wave operating at the speed of light. However, there is an important difference between the quantum mechanical description of a photon (massless) and an electron or any sub-atomic particle. Classical physics does not provide a law of motion for an electron particle (mass) or any mass particle in any related sense.

Into the breach of these and other peculiar sub-atomic particle behavior observations, Werner Heisenberg in 1927 postulated a theoretical principle addressing apparent sub-atomic particle uncertainties. The result of this principle is that our empirical ideas of reality were dramatically altered. This paper attempts an understanding of the uncertainty principle in relation to the region of the quantum.

Heisenberg's Uncertainty Principle

The literature describes Heisenberg's approach to the uncertainty principle as an exercise in matrix mechanics. In effect, the observables are not numbers that obey the laws of commutative arithmetic:

$$pq - qp = 0$$

But they are matrices or operators that obey the relationship:

$$pq - qp = H/i$$

where i squared = -1 and where H = h/2Π and where h = Planck's constant.

This complex matrix relationship represents Heisenberg's uncertainty principle. The scientific literature is clear that the uncertainty principle does not apply to mass and charge. The principle applies only to certain conjugate variables that cannot be measured simultaneously. (See Robert P. Crease and Alfred S. Goldhaber, *The Quantum Moment*.)

Observation on the Uncertainty Principle Dilemma

The uncertainty principle clearly expresses the impossibility of measuring exactly both position and momentum of sub-atomic particles. Unfortunately, this uncertainty has been interpreted to mean that sub-atomic particles do not have position and momentum. This idea of no meaning (ambiguous) is attributed to a scientific axiom that requires any physical concept to be described in terms of measurement. The uncertainty principle is upsetting to the scientific community because it undermines our idea of cause and effect.

Consequently, the nature of things "apparently" have no cause as they cannot be described completely in the present. This dilemma leads some scientists to conclude that the Universe is governed by imprecision and chance. However, mass and charge have perfectly definable and precise values in the sub-atomic world. The uncertainty principle applies only to specific conjugate variables. In effect, the principle restores a certain visualization at the cost of uncertainty.

As noted, Heisenberg's principle employs Bohr's idea of complementarity that describes something that can be a particle or a wave at the same time, but must always be measured to be either one or the other in any particular experiment. Measurements depend on the choice of the observer. Our empirical reality does not account for a physical reality beyond the senses, and simply expresses this quandary in terms of pure chance. Our concept of cause has no meaning in the atomic world. However, Heisenberg argued that his principle had repercussions even for the nature of reality itself and could lead to the conjecture that under the perceptible statistical world there is hidden a "real" world in which the causal law holds.

However, Heisenberg also added that such speculations are fruitless and meaningless. Physics should only describe formally the relation of perceptions. The uncertainty principle, as discussed by Crease and Goldhaber, is not just epistemological but ontological. It is not only what is known but what cannot be known. This philosophical rationale is certainly correct in a space-time model of reality and in an empirical sense. However, it is time to extend the boundaries of our empirical reality.

In this sense, my models hypothesize that it is self-evident that our space-time continuum was created. It was created through a purposeful plan and act by an eternal Creator. Consequently, it must logically follow that by this act of creation, our space-time continuum must contain an essence of the Creator's "whole" presence. By extension, and by the Creator's gift of cognition to its sentient creatures, it is philosophically reasonable and appropriate — perhaps even practical — to attempt an understanding of the essence of the creation process. It is certainly arguable that one purpose of our creation is to evolve. See my paper, "The Metaphysical Nature of the Creator."

A Five-Dimensional Perspective

To attempt an understanding of the complexity of uncertainty in our space-time model of reality, it is necessary to extend the concept of the space-time model to include a quantum reality beyond empirical considerations. (See my paper, "A Five-Dimensional Model of the Universe.")

My model hypothesizes that mass and matter are intricately related but separate entities, which function and operate in separate dimensions. Matter was created (derived) from mass through the auspices of the eternal calculus. Matter resides in our space-time continuum. It is a created entropic entity that is temporal in concept, operation, and function.

By contrast, mass functions in the fifth dimension. Mass is an eternal entity and is the physical operating component of the whole Universe.

It is noted that Dr. J.S. Bell offered a theorem that mathematically implies that the Universe is intimately and inextricably connected and linked. This theorem suggests the idea that Universal operating systems (mass-motion being the physical operating system, and the natural laws being the metaphysical operating system) provide the constant and efficient operation of the Creator's Universe.

Our space-time continuum was created. It was not created out of a vacuum nor was the creation a random event. It was an act of creation by an eternal Creator. This act of creation implies that the Creator is the functional operator of an eternal system in conjunction with a created entropic system. In this context, it is axiomatic that functional requirements for eternal/entropic systems require operational actions beyond empirical considerations.

The fundamental consideration here is that our entropic space-time system is a created reality derived from an eternal creation source — the Creator. In that sense, we do not control the cosmos. We are the observers of a complex, created reality. We operate in an attempt to understand the boundaries of our created system through the gift of cognition.

For instance, we observe that the speed of light is infinite in our space-time model. In fact, light is operating to the limit of its functional requirements within the scope of its entropic system. However, within the idea that the whole Universe is intimately connected, greater than light velocities may be required to facilitate immediate (instantaneous) functions and operations throughout the Universe.

As stated, we are the observers of this creation process. Our cognitive gifts allow us to speculate on the creation process, but we cannot instigate or control the natural law functions. We are not the Creator. There is an extraordinary difference between our cognitive ability to relate to an observational function in the whole of reality (mass-motion, the calculus, the opposites, apparent uncertainties) and the eternal natural functions that operate and perpetuate the whole Universe.

Conclusion

It is unfortunate that Heisenberg's brilliant interpretation of uncertainty in our space-time continuum is seen as implying imprecision in the Universe. The issue of uncertainty is not arguably related to imprecision or, for that matter, chaos. The problem in understanding this "apparent" uncertainty lies in our model of Newtonian reality. The idea that we can interpret complex quantum mechanics observables in an empirical space-time model will simply result in more confusion, misunderstanding, and misgivings. Our old model of reality was ruptured in 1900 with the discovery of the quanta and was shattered by Heisenberg's uncertainty principle related to sub-atomic particle behavior.

Scientific advancements in the technology of improved sensors are leading us closer to the interface of the quanta. This new complex region of the sub-atomic realm will test our cognitive powers to comprehend its nature and to explore the efficacy of my hypothetical fifth-dimensional model of reality.

Universal natural laws are immutable whether they operate in an eternal or entropic system. The particular parameters of the natural laws are governed by the functional requirements related to the specific system itself. As an example, the speed of light is infinite in space-time as an empirical concept. Its velocity is the limit of its functional needs and requirements in our entropic system. This does not imply that light (electromagnetic radiation) and its wave-length is the only operative source or velocity of communication in the Universe.

Uncertainty is an observable phenomenon in a related interplay of complex systems. Within the context of that observable phenomenon is the juxtaposition of a total reality separated by a dimension. A dimension that we cannot cross — certainly not in a physical sense — but perhaps one in which the prospect of a higher level of consciousness (an integration process) may permeate its border regions.

Correspondence on Uncertainty Principle with Peter Kearney (former Priest)

Kenneth,

The physics of your paper on Heisenberg's uncertainty principle is beyond what I can grasp. In the first paragraph under "Observation on the Uncertainty Principle Dilemma" which begins: "The idea of no meaning (ambiguous).... Is this part of the theory or is it your criticism of an erroneous viewpoint?

In the third paragraph of the same section, are you reporting what Heisenberg says or writing an inadequate understanding of him, or your own comments on Heisenberg?

Is your basic point in the paper that the Heisenberg principle applies only to certain pairs of variables (space-time) and is not applicable to all of reality? In particular, because the world of space-time is in constant decay, there is need of this dimension, the realm of mass-motion and the Creator. The consideration of this new dimension frees us from having to consider the Universe as subject only to uncertainties and movements of mere chance.

By the way, your observations have helped me with a book I am presently reading called *Christianity Without God*, written by an old friend who used to be a priest. He argues for the non-existence of God by showing that the eternal existence of the material world cannot be disproved and therefore we can think of the world as an evolution without need for a Creator.

Peter

Peter,

Thank you for reading my paper on Heisenberg's uncertainty principle and your always understanding and helpful questions.

The idea of an ambiguous meaning in my "observations" is simply based on the scientific community's response to Heisenberg's uncertainty principle as undermining our basic scientific ideas of cause and effect. It is not part of my theory nor any criticism on my part.

The fundamental point of my observation that empirical science does not account for a reality beyond the senses if that it is time to extend the boundaries of that empirical reality model. I simply reported the words of Heisenberg. I wanted to show that his brilliant observation on "uncertainty" led him philosophically to question the nature of reality. Yet he was constrained by rigorous discipline to ignore such speculations as fruitless and meaningless. Peter, this is the quandary of the reality of the senses vs. the reality of the natural laws.

You are correct: Heisenberg's principle is not applicable to all reality.

Yes, the fifth dimension obviates the need for us to be subject only to certainties and movements of mere chance. In fact, quantum physics has already theorized that mass and charge are not "uncertain" properties.

Christianity Without God provides an interesting concept. However, the word "God" is an intricate trap in the history of humankind. It's like boxing with shadows. To communicate its complexities is mind-shattering. In this sense, I prefer to use the term Creator — one Creator. However, the author's idea that the eternal existence of the material world cannot be disproved suggests that the material world is eternal. On this point, the material world is indisputably entropic — not eternal.

Kenneth

Correspondence with Larry Partain, Ph.D., Physicist, Translational Research Associates, on Uncertainty Principle

Ken,

I just read through your latest paper posted in your blog. I found some early statements distracting from what I think may be your major points. There is a statement that electrons do not obey the Classical laws of physics. Currently I am working on an X-ray tube that has an electron beam that strikes a tungsten target to produce the X-ray photons we use to track cancer lesion motion during radiotherapy. For this we describe and model the motion of electrons as particles exactly described by Newton's Laws of Motion to an extremely high accuracy. Its major advances are based on developments that treat electrons as being exactly described as particles controlled by Newton's Laws of motion. At another point you describe the speed of light as infinite. To the best of my knowledge, classical optics (telescopes, microscopes etc. using refraction) is explained by the speed of light having a very high but finite value that slows in in materials like glass compared to free space (or a vacuum).

It was great to hear again from you today by phone and to once again read through one of your blogs.

Larry

Larry,

Thank you for reading my latest paper and for your direct and honest comments and reactions regarding my ideas.

The Creator's Universal natural laws (all five dimensions) are immutable. If my comment in any way suggested otherwise, that would be in error.

My comment on the speed of light as infinite means only that its measured velocity cannot be <u>exceeded</u> in any entropic system. Its measured velocity is the absolute limit of its functional operation in our space-time continuum. The critical factor here is the term "functional operation." Whether the speed of light (depending on the experiment) can be altered/modified to some finite number is not related to my hypothesis as long as its infinite velocity is not exceeded. This does not preclude the possibility that super-luminal velocities are operational in the "whole" Universe. The idea of super-luminal velocities has been introduced by others and it just fits with my model of five-dimensional reality.

This conceptual idea needs to be pursued by the scientific community — hopefully you.

My hypothetical five-dimensional model does not imply or suggest that sub-atomic particles do not obey Universal natural laws. More to the point, particles and waves must follow three five-dimension Universal natural laws (i.e., the calculus, the laws of thermodynamics, etc.).

The essence of my arguments is that in the whole of the Universe (five-dimensions) we are confronted with both eternal and entropic systems. Efficient operations for these intimately related systems may be different and may require actions related to a specific functional demand. An example could be greater than the speed of light velocities for communication in the galaxies.

In terms of our empirical observations of the natural laws of the whole Universe, it would be a grave error to believe that we — collectively — fully understand the capability and depth of the natural laws operating in these complex systems of reality.

Kenneth

Ken,

This link is on quantum entanglement and may be of interest.

Quantum computer coding in silicon now possible. scienceblog.com.

A team of Australian engineers has proven — with the highest score ever obtained — that a quantum version of computer code can be written and manipulated, using quantum bits in a silicon microchip. The advance removes lingering doubts that such operations can be made reliably to allow powerful quantum computers to become a reality.

It makes me want to revisit our discussions on this topic and maybe even write the manuscript on quasi-random number simulation (a thought experiment) of quantum entanglement.

Larry

Larry,

Thank you for the paper on Quantum Links in space and time.

We have just returned from a three-week road trip to the southwest and are in the process of catching up with chores and projects.

This paper provides further observation and evidence that we need a new model of quantum reality beyond our empirical space-time continuum. The fact that scientists are observing phenomena like "quantum entanglement" and use terms like separate existence/shared existence indicates that we are on the cusp of acknowledging that Universal reality is more than a physical, empirical concept. On the downside, they keep referring to this perfectly natural entanglement phenomenon as "spooky action at a delay."

This paper is another reason why our quantum entanglement thought experiment regarding transmission at greater than the speed of light becomes intriguingly more important in supporting my quantum, five-dimensional model of Universal reality.

Kenneth

Complementarity — A Quantum Perspective

Introduction

The principle of complementarity was formulated by Niels Bohr. He considered a number of complementary properties in nature which included wave and particle related activities (light), the focus of this paper's attention.

A quote attributed to Albert Einstein and Leopold Infield asks: "But what is light really? Is it a wave or a shower or photons? We have two contradictory pictures of reality. Separately, neither of them fully explains the phenomenon of light, but together they do."

The principle of complementarity is a natural universal phenomenon that is presently being understood in terms of our empirical (space/time model) of reality. In this sense, it becomes a paradox — and will always be a paradox. If we expand our classical physics models to incorporate a quantum perspective to understand wave and particle behavior in nature, we may begin to have an understanding of the functions and the nature of universal reality.

Complementarity Principle — From the Literature

The principle of complementarity states that particular objects have certain pairs of complementary properties which cannot all be observed or measured simultaneously. The particle and wave aspects of light are such a complementary phenomenon. By extension, from classical mechanics, it is impossible for these aspects to be a particle and a wave at the same time. In this sense, it is impossible to measure the full properties of the wave and particle at a particular moment. An aspect of complementarity is that it not only applies to measurability or knowability of some property of a physical entity, but more importantly it applies to the limitations of that physical entity's manifestation of the property in the physical world. Physical reality is determined and defined by manifestations of properties which are limited by trade-offs between these complementary pairs. Complementarity and uncertainty (note Heisenberg principle) dictate that all properties and actions in the physical world manifest themselves as non-deterministic to some degree.

From this complementarity principle, we begin the process of understanding light as both a particle phenomenon and a wave phenomenon in a quantum perspective.

Complementarity — Wave or Particle

The Wave Form of Light

Light is energy. Its operational functions can be complicated by introducing the interaction of electric and magnetic fields, but fundamentally light is energy.

The wave form of light is directly related to a range of frequencies (wavelengths) of light vibrations. Light waves specifically operate in our empirical system (space-time) that limits its operation to a spectrum of frequencies and related finite parameters. Ordinarily light as a wave function describes a sensory pattern of visible spectrum reality constrained by the limitations of our classical space-time reality. The behavior of light as a wave function (massless) is operationally limited in our space-time model at the rate of 186,000 miles per second. In this case, the speed of light is limited by the laws of Special Relativity.

Light is also electromagnetic radiation within a certain portion of the electromagnetic spectrum. In a human sense, this usually refers to visible light — the spectrum that is visible to human eyesight. Light waves are an empirical (massless) form of energy.

The Particle Form of Light

Light behaves as a particle in an eternal quantum system. (See my paper: "A Five-Dimensional Model of the Universe.") According to quantum mechanics, light can be viewed as a collection of particles (photons). However, in classical electromagnetic theory, photons are considered to have no rest mass (photons cannot be brought to rest), so these "particles" of light are considered massless. In that classical theory sense, physicists use this massless "figure of speech" to characterize how photon "particle like" properties are described using the theory of Special Relativity. This massless interpretation provides a convenient mechanism to apply both matter and "particles of light" in a similar general equation.

Do photons have any mass at all? If light is confined by the laws of Special Relativity and always travels at the speed of light (considered infinite), then we are back to classical physics and convenient mathematical equations based on wave theory.

In a quantum sense, rest mass is always the same for the same type of particle. All protons have identical rest masses, as do all electrons, neutrons, etc. As particles are accelerated to greater speeds, then relativistic mass increases without limit. The boundaries of light in an empirical (entropic) <u>matter</u> system are not necessarily constrained by the functional operational requirements of an eternal (non-entropic) <u>mass</u> system.

In classical physics, light always travels at the same speed. In that sense, the speed of light is considered constant (c). This constant speed is characteristic of operational behavior in a created entropic system. Light is always a wave function (massless) in an entropic system — and its speed is constant at c.

In a quantum non-entropic system, light is described as utilizing particle energy (mass) for its functional operation. This complementarity activity may require functional light behavior beyond the limits of the constant entropic speed at c.

The prevailing scientific position is that the complementarity of light (wave/particle) can be interpreted by the claim that photons are particles and that they are massless. If that position is correct, then photons are wave functions — not particle functions. All particles have mass. In that case, complementarity in relation to light must seek another solution — perhaps in the investigation of the energy behavior of electrons or photon mass related experiments.

Conclusion

Again, from Bohr's and Heisenberg's studies, complementarity and uncertainty dictate that therefore all properties and actions in the physical world manifest themselves as non-deterministic to some degree. Bohr and Heisenberg are, in fact, implying that our present models of classical physics (space-time) are limited to empirical explanations.

The quantum world ushered in one hundred and twenty years ago from Max Planck's experiments on black bodies has left the scientific community still mired in our empirical space-time model of the whole of reality. Scientific quantum data (in this case, complementarity and uncertainty) are ordinarily shoe-horned into a classical physics model to explain and relate to an approximate empirical perspective. Science is then confronted with dilemmas and paradoxes — inexplicable physical behavior presented in terms of our classical physics model of reality. In quantum terms, there are no dilemmas or paradoxes in the nature of things. The natural laws that govern the <u>functional</u> operation of a created entropic system in conjunction with an eternal non-entropic system are immutable. (See my paper "A Five-Dimensional Model of the Universe.") My model hypothesizes a quantum-based perspective that explores the relationship between operating entropic and non-entropic systems.

Complementarity is present in reality because we are dealing with two separate operating systems with particular and distinct functions.

Light is a wave in our created space-time (entropic) system. Light behaves as a particle in a quantum (non-entropic) system. They are both functional entities in their respective dimensional realms. Their particular functions in the Universe describe their behavioral patterns in managing the operational requirements for an efficient universal whole.

51

Letter on Complementarity from Larry Partain, Ph.D. Physicist, Translational Research Associates

Ken,

Thanks for alerting me to your latest blog that I just read. I particularly liked your description of Bohr's concepts of complementarity. If one works with solar cells like I have for many years, light is made of photons that add up like one-by-one particles to create the electric current that flows out of them. Thus a solar cell and its exposure to photons are "converted" at a single place and point in time to provide renewable energy in huge quantities from the sun. This contrasts to the light imaged by the Hubble space telescope which come from continuous light waves going back almost to the 14 billion light-years age of time and space when the big bang occurred and are not confined to a single place or point in time. Thus it makes no sense to try and address a photon as a wave and as a massless (but not energy-less) particle at the same time. In my two books titled "Solar Cells and Their Applications" (two editions published by Wiley in 1995 and 2010), I do a quantum mechanical derivation of their current-voltage properties of solar cells which determines how much energy and power you can get from them. However to get their voltage properties, I have to use the Schrodinger's wave equation that is logical non-sense if you try and use them to calculate the solar cell current. Without apology, I use this logically contradictory process. You very clearly state that they have to be taken as separate and logically incompatible concepts that only make sense when considered separately (not simultaneously) and I agree. However once I have this equation, I use it to simultaneously describe both the current and voltage of solar cells, but without shame. Otherwise there is no currently accurate equation that describes how solar cells work. This is part of the gut wrenching concepts that allows modern science to treat major properties of our current world permeated by illogical (and contradictory) quantum mechanical issues. Good read. Thanks.

Larry

A Quantum Perspective on the Schrodinger's Cat Experiment

Introduction

Schrodinger's cat is a thought experiment devised by the physicist Edwin Schrodinger in 1935. The experiment involves placing a living cat into a chamber containing a closed vial of hydrocyanic acid. There is also a trace of radioactive hydrocyanic acid in the chamber. If a single atom of that substance were to decay during the test period, a relay would trip to break the vial and kill the cat. The observer cannot know if an atom of the acid has decayed and cannot know whether the vial was broken, the acid released, and whether the cat is dead or alive. The answer cannot be known until the observer opens the box and determines the cat's state of being (alive or dead).

Ordinarily, the simple matter of resolving the issue is to open the box and determine the result of any radioactive decay under experiment. However, Schrodinger did not devise this thought experiment as a simple interpretation of classical physics (empirical logic), but rather to challenge the existing views (perspective) of quantum mechanics. Particularly, he wanted to challenge the subject of the EPR (Einstein, Podolsky, and Rosen) paper in 1935 on the nature of quantum superpositions. The EPR paper discussed the nature of quantum systems where an atom or photon can exist as a combination of states with different outcomes. The theory was called the Copenhagen interpretation. Schrodinger understood that the Copenhagen interpretation means that the cat remained both dead and alive until the state is observed. He intended to point out the absurdity of the quantum mechanics perspective. He argued the impossibility of the cat being alive and dead at the same time.

Following the disagreement between Schrodinger and the EPR paper, particularly as it relates to the superposition of particles in multiple states, the interpretation of the cat experiment was further complicated and obscured by its notoriety. Myriad explanations that followed the experiment included the many worlds view, the Ensemble and Relation interpretation, along with objective collapse theories, and others.

Schrodinger was distraught over the confusion that emerged from his experiment along with the resultant paradox that hangs over the idea of a cat being dead and alive at the same time.

A Quantum Perspective

Since the quantum theory of superposition (as it relates to the EPR paper) was the catalyst for Schrodinger's cat experiment, the focus of this paper is to interpret his thought experiment in relation to a quantum model perspective.

The EPR paper somehow became linked to the prevailing quantum theory (the Copenhagen interpretation) that highlighted the curious nature of quantum "superpositions" that connected particle behavior in multiple states.

It is unfortunate that Schrodinger interpreted the quantum world (sub-atomic particles) as operationally the same as our empirical (space-time) world. This view carries the expectation that a cat can be substituted for sub-atomic particles and that alive or dead means the same thing for both entities. This view introduces a logical fallacy into the equation depending on the model of reality under investigation. Admittedly, the quantum world of 1935 (when the EPR paper was written) was in its infancy and the scientific community never suggested that an evolving quantum theory (in this case the EPR paper) was a complete explanation of quantum reality. More than 80 years later, quantum theory models of reality continue to struggle for recognition against the limitations of classical physics — our empirical reality.

In response, I have postulated a hypothesis which expands our space-time continuum model (four dimensions) to a five-dimensional model of the Universe. (See my paper: "A Five-Dimensional Model of the Universe"). As our technology advances, we move closer to the interface of the created, entropic world of matter-time to a non-entropic mass-motion world of sub-atomic particle reality. Specifically, my quantum model expands our space-time continuum to a mass-motion, matter-time concept. Mass-motion are fifth-dimensional, non-entropic entities, and matter-time are created entropic entities derived (auspices of the natural calculus) from a creation event. Through this lens, the Schrodinger cat experiment takes on a complex dimensional relationship. It is seen to have two operationally independent perspectives:

First, in an entropic space-time model, the experiment proceeds as set up by Schrodinger. The results (life and/or death for the cat) are determined by sensate observations related to events that may or may not have occurred until the box is opened and the results revealed. This experimental perspective is the nature and is the natural operating function of an entropic space-time system.

Second, the experiment becomes more complicated when considering the idea of a mass-motion eternal system. Now we must consider the principle of superposition in quantum theory that occurs at the sub-atomic level. These superposition occurrences are observable effects of interference where a particle is demonstrated to be in multiple locations simultaneously. This quantum condition has complicated the nature of reality on the observable level (cats as opposed to particles) and is perhaps the most profound paradox in quantum physics.

As a consequence, this indeterminacy or observer's paradox was not an acceptable concept for Schrodinger or others. His argument that the cat cannot be alive and dead at the same time (it defies logic) underlies his position.

However, following our hypothetical eternal mass-motion model we can no longer accept that sub-atomic particles can be the substituted equivalent of a cat in a box. Sub-atomic particle functions are not limited to operations in matter-time, but include functions in the operation of the whole Universe as part of their non-entropic process. Sub-atomic particles are non-entropic entitles that have no meaning in terms of life or death — or time. They operate to fulfill the natural functions of both entropic and non-entropic systems.

The question becomes a matter of what are the functions of a non-entropic system and by extension what are the natural functions that operate our created entropic space-time system. On the one hand, science has been exploring the nature of our created space-time continuum since Aristotle. There is a library of data on the empirical world. Now, a quantum world of reality has been opened to us since the extraordinary experiments on black boxes by Max Planck in 1900. A new quantum science was introduced to the world of physics. Now, questions related to both entropic and nonentropic systems are open to exploration along with speculation on the integration of separate and distinct universal operational functions.

New quantum models of reality are required for this exploration — models that attempt to clarify apparent physical anomalies rather than mystify the process with strict empirical models.

Schrodinger's cat experiment is not a paradox in the sense of a quantum interpretation. The idea of superposition in quantum theory that creates a situation called indeterminacy (observer's paradox) will always be a paradox in terms of an empirical sense of reality. It is, however, a puzzle only in the sense where mass and matter (while fundamentally related) are modeled as the same entity, operating in the same dimension and under the exact same fundamental requirements for universal operation.

Conclusion

Schrodinger played a complicated game with his colleagues along with the classical physics definition of physical reality. He extrapolated that empirical model to include the uncertainty of life and death and time related events — cat in a box.

However, his experiment did not account for a reality beyond the empirical into a quantum world of reality, which posited the idea of multiple sub-atomic states (superposition) at the same time. Unfortunately he translated a complex quantum function into an empirical idea of "alive and dead at the same time." He lived in the reality of the classical physics model and found the concept of alive and/or dead as an absurd impossibility. However, in his interpretation of classical physics models and language definitions, his conclusions made perfect sense.

Historically, our western scientific development (our technological advances) have followed a path toward sensate and empirical concepts since the seeds of physical reality were highlighted by Aristotle in his ideas of experiments and the careful measurement of the scientific method. Paradoxically, the physical world owes the empirical roots of its broad intellectual acceptance to a philosopher.

However, as our technology expands and leads us closer to the sub-atomic realm, this quantum world is now providing us with anomalies and instances of events that "seem" to be contradictory to our comfortable sensate experience. These natural anomalies cannot be resolved in empirical terms alone. In that respect they become paradoxes and conundrums.

A quantum reality is required to understand our expanding world of science. It is not possible for a thermodynamically entropic system to self-perpetuate or to regenerate itself without non-entropic energy. Mass-motion is an efficient, non-entropic physical operating system. In conjunction with universal natural laws, it operates the "whole" of our Universe including our created, space-time system.

Correspondence on Schrodinger's Cat with Larry Staples, Ph.D., Jungian Analyst

Kenneth,

I have no idea what "quantum superpositions" are, and it grows more difficult when you add "superposition of particles in multiple states." The phrase "auspices of the natural calculus" eludes me. You say the Schrodinger cat experiment takes on a complex dimensional relationship from two operationally independent perspectives.

I think I do grasp what is one of your ideas: that the existing world would dwindle to nothing if it were the beneficiary of an infusion of energy from some unseen source of matter. So, your ideas lead you toward a kind of scientific explanation of an invisible creative power behind all the visible world. It seems to me that this journey of discovery leads you to realms not imagined by most people. Whether I understand the enormously complex constructs that you introduce, I feel that there are people — if you can find them — that may understand and appreciate your theses and their explanations.

Larry

Larry,

Thank you for reading my latest paper. I appreciate your efforts at assimilating some of these abstract concepts.

Let's begin with what you know. Yes, our empirical world (space-time) would continue a process of decay (an entropic condition) unless it was the beneficiary of an infusion of energy from a non-entropic (eternal) system. In our local solar system, the sun will expire in some cataclysmic phase, probably resulting in a dead star.

To your questions:

1. "The auspices of the natural calculus"

My view is that the calculus is an eternal, natural law. It is not theorized, it was not invented, it was brilliantly discovered in nature. The calculus (the metaphysical concept) is pervasive in the whole of the Universe — it operates in the same way a thousand light years away.

2. "Two operationally independent perspectives"

We are dealing with related but different models of reality. In this case, the classical physics model we call space-time and my hypothetical quantum model that I call the fifth dimension. It is vital here to understand that any theory or hypothesis of physical/metaphysical reality — in an absolute philosophical sense — are simply models that are useful operational tools for the experimental progress and the physical/metaphysical understanding of the "whole" of reality. As an example, the classical physics space-time model is an almost perfect tool for experimenting and exploring our limited, empirical (created) world of reality.

3. "The cat experiment takes on a complex dimension relationship"

I am saying that Schrodinger lived in a classical physical world of empirical reality (four dimensional). He sees mass and matter as the same thing. He believes that you can substitute a cat for sub-atomic particle behavior in an experiment and get the same results. There are dimensional and functional differences in mass and matter operations.

4. "Superpositions of particles in multiple states"

Hold onto your hat! Superposition is a quantum theory related to behavior of sub-atomic particles. Superposition is an apparent anomaly whereby the strange nature of a quantum system (a sub-atomic particle) can exist as a combination of multiple states related to different possible outcomes. Its quantum "states" could be interpreted as a particle being in two or more places at the same time (separated by large distances — light years) whose outcome (change of state) is determined by its function. My quantum model would certainly support the proposition of "superposition" particularly as it relates to the efficient functional operation of a mass-motion eternal system.

Now, Schrodinger tried to interpret this quantum anomaly to an empirical concept. His idea was to consider "states" as related to alive or dead or both at the same time — enter the cat.

Kenneth

Correspondence with Larry Partain, Ph.D. Physicist, on Schrodinger's Cat

Ken,

I just reread your Schrodinger Cat paper with fascination. All the controversies you well describe have never really gone away with time. Reading through your paper brings back all the discomfort I have had for quantum mechanics since I first took a detailed course on it in graduate school. It is amazing that quantum mechanics is so accurate in describing and guiding the development of, let's say solar cells, but yet so illogical in terms of "basic common sense" and in terms of almost any ordinary experiences we observe in a macroscopic world. I keep hoping that your fifth dimension hypothesis might help lead us to a better and more comfortable space.

Entropy applies to both the classical macroscopic world and also to the microscopic quantum mechanical world. Entropy is basically a measure of disorder in both "worlds". In a closed "world" entropy always increases. When a cat dies, its entropy increases as it immediately begins to decay into a more disordered state than a live cat - eventually into "dirt". When a radioactive material decays by emitting radiation photons, the remaining decayed material is more disordered. Eventually all the radioactive atoms decay into non-radioactive states that are more "disordered" and thus to a higher entropy value.

Larry

Larry,

Thank you for reading my paper and your incisive question on entropy and the natural thermodynamic laws.

From the literature:

- Entropy, the second law of thermodynamics, is a fundamental law of physics.
- Entropy is a principle of thermodynamics that deals with energy.
- It is a measure of a particular system disorder.
- Lately, a new recognition called MEP (maximum entropy production) expands the law to show that spontaneous production of order from disorder is the expected

consequence of these basic laws. The law should not be thought of as simply a process of disorder. Entropy becomes a subject not only of physics but also of all of life and cognition. I agree with the above. However, my models would postulate that entropy is an empirical concept in the sense that its thermodynamic functions (its natural laws) are operationally directed to created systems. Our space-time continuum is a created system and its nature is entropic. And its corollary is that it cannot create. In contrast, the fifth dimension is an eternal system and its physical components (mass-motion) are eternal entities. Their operational functions include both the eternal and the created systems. These operational functions are complex and are not limited or molded by empirical considerations or limitations.

The behavior of sub-atomic particles is not predictable in the sense of their complex functions for the operations of entropic and eternal (by definition non-entropic) systems. In the case of Schrodinger's cat, sub-atomic particles cannot be presumed to be directly substituted for a "cat" in the experiment since they have no meaning (different dimensions) in terms of life or death — or time.

Science so aptly uses the term "space-time continuum" as opposed to tackling the complex relationship between mass and matter in a quantum sense of reality.

Kenneth

The Relationship Between Motion and Time

Introduction

My five-dimensional model of the Universe hypothesizes that motion and time are separate entities characterized by a relativisitic relationship. The model implies that time is an implicit derivative of motion. In that change of state (dimensional shift), these entities are fundamentally different in function and in purpose. Motion is an eternal concept in a five-dimensional Universal construct while time is a temporal concept in a four-dimensional empirical sense of reality. In this regard, it is important to consider the unique relationship between motion and time to better understand their respective functions and purposes operating in a five-dimensional sense of reality.

Motion

Motion is an eternal, Universal constant. Motion is pervasive and permeates any sense or perception of reality. Its activity is the catalyst for the function and operation of the whole Universe. Without constant, precise motion, the physical operating component (mass) of our five-dimensional Universe would be cataclysmically ruptured. The absence of motion is a Universal impossibility as would be the concept of an absolute solid.

Motion permeates all of our five-dimensional Universe. It is pervasive in any sense of reality and always operates in accord with its Universal natural laws. Motion is the catalyst for any concept or system of regenerative reality — including our empirical space-time continuum or my hypothetical five-dimensional Universe.

Motion, operating in its primary fifth-dimensional function, is always a precise, constant (i.e., eternal) entity. It is not limited by spatial considerations or time-related directions. In this sense, motion is a state of precise, active functioning (the action or process of changing positions) with the inherent ability or power to move. The fifth dimension is the operator of the whole of the Universe and its natural laws function to promote the stability and the normal operation of the total Universal system, including our implicitly derived space-time continuum. Our space-time continuum is an entropic system interconnected with all the galaxies comprising the total of all our empirical, space-time sense of reality. Our empirical connection to the fifth dimension (the operator of the Universal whole) is fundamentally a derivative (a change of state) process. The fifth dimension operates the whole of our Universe as an eternal, non-entropic system. The whole of the Universe (i.e., five dimensions) is governed by natural laws non- related to chaotic conditions, except that our space-time continuum is a temporal, entropic entity.

Motion pre-existed our empirical sense of reality and is an eternal concept. Motion is the catalyst from which mass produces energy. Motion is a non-entropic fifth-dimensional entity. However, motion also operates as an empirical entity (space-time continuum) as a related consequence of the derivation of motion to time.

Time

The general definition of time is given as a non-spatial continuum in which events occur in irreversible succession. Time regulates, adjusts, and records the orderly sequence of movements or duration of events. Beyond this definition, I hypothesize in my five-dimensional model of the Universe that time is a complex, empirical dimension. Time actuates and records the history of our space-time continuum as it progresses through its evolutionary development process. Further, time is an implicit derivation of motion and functions as a temporal entity in our space-time continuum sense of reality. Time records the actions put into place by the creation of space-time and, by extension, the cognitive progression of all its sentient creatures.

Time is a temporal entity directly and relativistically interactive with its spatial coordinates (a functional continuum). Time is interdependent with its spatial continuum and will cease when matter (its temporal extension) ceases.

Motion-Time Functions

In an empirical sense, it is difficult to comprehend the fully functional concept of motion without time. We address the concept of motion in the guise of time. We speak of measuring motion (or understanding it) in relation to time. Our observation of movement through space at some velocity is an empirical time concept.

Motion transcends the time concept as the Creator's catalyst for action. (See my paper, "The Creator Model.") Motion provides the energy transfer action for any or all Universal functions, including space-time. It is an omnidirectional concept related to time (its derivative), but it operationally provides a different Universal task as the catalyst for the operation of the Universe. The function of time is to record the physical history of our created space-time continuum and to record the cognitive evolutionary progress of sentient beings.

Conclusion

To review, my five-dimensional mode of the Universe hypothesizes that motion is an eternal Universal constant, and time is an implicit derivative of motion and is a temporal concept in a four-dimensional empirical sense of reality. Motion and time are relativistically linked, but their implicit differences are in form and function. The operational function of fifth-dimensional motion is precise, constant, eternal Universal activity. Again, the primary functions of time are to record the activities/actions from the dawn of creation of our empirical four-dimensional sense of reality along with the cognitive progression of sentient creatures.

Our five-dimensional Universe is a complex system in motion operating in accord with the natural laws of the Creator. The whole of the Universe is subject to these natural laws and, by extension, to our temporal, empirical space-time reality.

Correspondence on Time and Motion with Larry Partain, Ph.D. Physicist, Translational Research Associates

Ken,

I have just reread your Time and Motion paper. The terms and relationships you describe are so unfamiliar that I have a hard time getting my mind around the unique concepts you propose. It is not that I disagree with your statements. It is just difficult for me to relate them to some physics/engineering starting point where I feel a high degree of confidence. I feel much the same difficulty when I read and try to understand Einstein's general relativity where mass produces curvatures in space and time and light no longer moves in straight lines. When this calculated value was compared to the shifted positions of stars observed during a solar eclipse, the measured shifts agreed with Einstein's prediction. Before this experimental verification, Einstein's theory was thought experiments that initially were just philosophy. Philosophy is not bad. It was the Greek starting point for all of modern science as recognized by doctoral degrees being called Ph.D.'s. I keep trying to think of experimental ways to test what you propose but so far without success. As you come up with more related concepts and models, I will keep trying to think of possible tests.

Larry

Larry,

Thank you for your comments on my latest paper. I appreciate the time and perspective you have offered to my models that extend our universal sense of reality. I note, however, that you have mentioned your struggle relating the idea of philosophy with the vital acceptance of reproducible experimentation on several occasions.

Allow me to comment on your concerns. Aristotle is arguably the father of what we understand as our present scientific model of reality (our space-time continuum). His philosophy (the physical world of reality) was cobbled together over hundreds of years by brilliant observers (Newton, et al.) of the nature of things into an extraordinary model of empirical reality — the Universe of the sensate (our space-time continuum). However, this space-time continuum is a hypothetical model of reality. It is a hypothesis based on the concept of physical reality. Bohr's work on the hydrogen atom is another of many examples of a model of elemental reality that has proven useful in understanding our physical world (space-time), but they are hypothetical empirical concepts. My models are hypothetical concepts garnered from sixty-plus years of observations and abstract reasoning. They do not purport to be the whole universal truth. They are like the Creator's clay. They need to be worked and molded.

I am a staunch advocate for the requirement of physical presence in any concept of universal reality. I'm trying to push the peanut down the road! Our society has been the fortunate recipient of the output of Newtonian physics based on observation and experimentation. Now, however, our technology is pushing the envelope (i.e. boundaries) of our space-time continuum into a new dimension. As our tools for more precise experimentation evolve, we will begin to confront the mysteries of the complex nature of the whole Universe. Science, which really began with Planck's experiments on black bodies in 1900, is really in its infancy.

Kenneth

Correspondence on Time and Motion with Larry Staples, Ph.D., Jungian Analyst

Ken,

I did a quick read of your motion/time piece this morning and quickly realized I need your help with something, if I am to have any hope of understanding it. I'm not sure what you mean by entropic. As you know, there are multiple definitions of entropy, all of which may be loosely related. I think I can dismiss the one that says entropy is a measure of the loss of information in a transmitted message. The applicability of other definitions to your paper can be a closer call. I think you can see just from this simple question about what scientists would likely be perfectly obvious.

Larry

Larry,

Ah! entropy. There is no such thing as a simple question as it relates to entropy. It is the "gut" issue in hypothesizing a five-dimensional model of the Universe, where our space-time continuum is an entropic system, and the fifth dimension is the non-entropic creator of our "whole reality" system. Entropy in space-time is simply a measure of disorder in that system as it undergoes a spontaneous change expressed as a mathematical, thermodynamic relationship. In this sense, entropy is a scientifically proven, empirical concept — no argument here. However, the fun is just beginning!

Assuming my hypothetical fifth dimension were an entropic system, then the whole of reality would be temporal and our Universe would eventually become a void. The Creator, mass/motion, and the natural laws would cease. My paper on "The Void Concept" tried to address this issue and concluded that the Creator is eternal and, by extension, so are its natural laws and mass/motion. We are left to conclude that either a non-entropic system (hypothetically, a fifth dimension) created (derived) our space-time continuum, or our entropic space-time system created itself and is an eternal concept — an entropic absurdity.

Kenneth

Thermodynamic Entropy

Introduction

To understand the natural law of thermodynamic entropy, it is necessary to focus on the properties of matter — particularly as it relates to both empirical and quantum models of reality. Matter is the physical output from the creation of empirical reality. By extension, science long ago investigated the molecular structure of matter as comprising a stable configuration of atomic nuclei and electrons (our present model of atomic particle theory), bound together by electrostatic and electromagnetic forces. The molecule represents the simplest structural unit that displays the characteristic physical and chemical properties of a compound. The molecule is the essence of the creation of empirical reality — the property of matter. These physical entities are somewhat complicated by the introduction of elements which are described as irreducible, fundamental constituents of a composite entity. However, molecules and elements represent the essential structure of created matter.

This paper will confine itself to considering entropy in relation to the second law of thermodynamics as a fundamental law of empirical nature. However, the study of entropy has been expanded from its core meaning and definition into several theoretically related disciplines such as cryptography, random number generators, statistics, etc., but these interpretations may have clouded our understanding of the natural law of entropy. It is in the nature of empirical reality that this paper attempts to provide an understanding of entropy as a closed system evolving and inexorably increasing toward a state of maximum disorder.

Definition

Entropy is introduced in the literature as the measure of a system thermal energy per unit temperature that is unavailable for doing useful work. Work is obtained from ordered molecular motion. The amount of entropy is also the measure of the molecular disorder, or randomness, of a system. The second law of thermodynamics usually refers to the idea that everything in the empirical Universe moves from order to disorder, and that entropy is the measure of that change (always increasing). Further, we are discussing closed entropic empirical systems evolving towards a state of maximum entropy — in fact, toward a state of their own temporal demise.

The Eternal System

An attempt to hypothesize entropy as an empirical concept must, by definition, require the introduction of an eternal system operating in conjunction with a created entity.

We are connected to all of reality through the Creation process. In that strict sense, we are connected to the Creator. Correspondingly, we are part of an entropic system, along with being connected to a functionally related eternal system. We cannot be disconnected from either reality.

Human life, as we interpret it in an empirical world, primarily constitutes sense observations, including our ecosystem, its reproductive activities, and all its manifestations that we sense as our physical reality. We are hurtling through space on a life-giving ecological platform for some real or imagined purpose. What curious and complex process is laid before us in our creation? What can we understand beyond the physical? Fortunately, we have been introduced to the nature of reality even in this simple ecological aspect of life. The laws of nature have been provided to lead us from the physical world to a complex world of cognition and its wondrous implications and possibilities of discovery.

Hypothetically, entropy is a product of an empirical system. Further, it is a product of a created system. Its functional operation within the context of that creation process utilizes the thermodynamic law of its empirical nature. Entropy does not and cannot operate in an eternal system. There would be no functional need for the "whole" of nature to embrace entropy.

Paradoxically, entropy is now being studied in reference to the relationship of information theory to thermodynamics. The thrust of this work is connected to the limitations of circuit miniaturization and reversible operations. The work relates to Landauer's principle that the erasure of data stored in a system has an inherent work cost and therefore dissipates heat. Certainly, in a classical physical sense (matter), this principle is arguably correct — it meets the criteria of the laws of entropy.

However, when quantum information, particularly when quantum memory entanglement is introduced in the system, Landauer's principle somehow strangely seems to have been invalidated and the outcome is curiously interpreted as "negative entropy." Negative entropy in the quantum case is hypothesized as being correlated to a system that gains work — cooling the environment. This interpretation of quantum entanglement would suggest that these investigations are observing quantum operations (entanglement) within the confines of the natural laws of empirical entropy. Moreover, this quantum entanglement hypothesis is clearly stating that all of universal reality is defined by an entropic (empirical) system. We have come full circle back to classical physics as the definition of the whole of reality. We are again reaching beyond the totally efficient system, toward the super-efficient system that surpasses natural perfection — in a created, entropic classical model of reality. The question, however, is whether we understand the natural functions of quantum entanglement as it relates to a total universal reality beyond our created, entropic system. From this limited perspective, we need to hypothesize a non-entropic system: A system that is eternal and recognizes the creation and re-creation processes that enfold all of reality. The law of entropy plays its temporal role as an always increasing entity in the temporal history of the galaxies.

Entropy has no relationship to an efficient system in an empirical sense of reality — it cannot function in that environment. By extension, it cannot create. It simply replicates its DNA. The only connection to a totally efficient system must, by definition, be an eternal concept. Further, a totally efficient system will only be exposed in reality through the recognition that inefficiency (entropy) is not a viable entity in the eternal order of reality.

Conclusion

Entropy is hypothesized as a fundamental law of nature in a created, empirical system. In contrast, if we assume that the classical model of reality (space-time) is the "whole" of reality, then all of reality is an illusion, since an entropic system is not capable of creation or re-creation of and by itself. This simple statement poignantly argues for a relativistic relationship between an eternal creation system (see my paper: "The Creator's Realm") in conjunction with our created entropic system.

Entropy has no physical function in an eternal system. Its operational quotient is zero. Entropy would be an absurd concept in an eternal system. This argument puts the question in the form of a quandary: Either rationalize that space-time (matter) has always existed (is eternal) or that the second law of thermodynamics (entropy) is refuted.

Corresponence on Thermodynamic Entropy with Larry Partain, Ph.D. Physicist, Translational Research Associates

Ken,

The most striking aspect to me of your latest blog on entropy and universal reality is your discussion that quantum mechanics may justify a concept of a negative entropy. At entropy's higher values there are many accessible states. As I recall entropy is actually the logarithm of the number of accessible states. The highest order (and lowest disorder) is when there is a single state and the logarithm of one is always zero (the absolute minimum for entropy). However if one takes the logarithm of a fraction (that is less than one), its logarithm always negative and the log of zero is minus infinity. To a degree maybe one can consider that quantum mechanics could introduce fractional accessible states (whatever that might be). Since you and I took college courses on the building blocks of material being protons, neutrons and electrons, that constitute all the atoms and molecules of matter, they now talk about "up" and "down" quarks that never exist in isolation. When there are two "ups" and one "down" the result is a proton. Maybe such quarks are something of a fractional accessible state where two "downs" and one "up" makes up a neutron. As always your writings always stimulate my mind and imagination to consider new concepts in ways that I always find stimulating and interesting.

Thanks, Larry

Larry,

Thank you for reading my paper on thermodynamic entropy.

The natural laws of the whole Universe (according to my models) will not justify a concept of a negative entropy — whether it be in a created system (empirical) or in an eternal system. My critical argument is that the whole of reality comprises both an entropic system and an eternal system. The key operative word for any activity involving entropy in an eternal system is function. Entropy has no function in an eternal system — zero energy.

The idea of thermodynamic entropy being applied to a study of information theory, particularly when it conjures up some curious idea of "negative entropy" that implies an efficency (supra) beyond total efficiency is simply a classical physics interpretation of the function of quantum entanglement. They simply do not understand the concept of an eternal system and its quantum entanglement. The natural laws of the whole Universe are not constructed to be confused by some misuse of their function in a created entropic reality. The investigators are four-dimension empiricists.

My point of introducing information theory to the natural laws of entropy is to point out the confusion and the pitfalls latent in any scientific study that will not accept the hypothesis of an etermal system operating in conjunction with an entropic system.

Kenneth

A Quantum Perspective On "Dark Matter"

Introduction

The scientific community is traditionally tasked to seek solutions to particular natural phenomena, usually by way of providing repeatable experimental results. In engineering terms, we might consider these experimental solutions as applying "adaptive principles" to a particular problem. These principles include the use of the physical resources at our disposal along with the observed laws of nature to direct and experimentally verify our engineering progress toward useful outcomes. The collaboration of "adaptive principles" becomes the driver for experimental and empirical scientific progress.

In our scientific process of discovery, the investigators utilize materials that make up the nature of our empirical reality. These components are intrinsically linked — inseparable. The point is that these "adaptive principles" are directly linked to the sensate world we inhabit. However, these principles must extend to and include new models of the quantum world that will provide further scientific understanding not only to our created, empirical world but also to all of universal reality.

A quantum perspective on the "dark matter" hypothesis requires a model of physical reality beyond our classical four-dimensional empirical concept. In this perspective, it is imperative to investigate and understand the integral relationship between created entropic matter and eternal mass. Refer to my paper "A Five-Dimensional Model of the Universe."

The Hypothesis

From the scientific literature, "dark matter" is considered a hypothetical type of matter. It has never been directly observed, but its existence is a part of certain puzzling astronomical observations. Its name refers to the fact that it does not emit or interact with electromagnetic radiation (light) and is invisible to the entire electromagnetic spectrum. Its properties are inferred from gravitational effects such as the motion of matter (baryonic), the influence on the Universe's large-scale structure (formation of galaxies), and its effect on the cosmic microwave background (CMB). Ordinary matter (baryonic) and "dark matter" are not characterized by the same behavioral patterns in that ordinary matter interacts with electromagnetic radiation, while "dark matter" does not react. Ordinary and "dark" matter leave different imprints on CMB.

Of significance here is the observational evidence from galaxies, particularly spiral galaxies, that rotate around the galactic center. The luminous mass density of a spiral galaxy decreases from the center to its outskirts. From Kepler's second law, we should expect that the rotational velocities will decrease with distance from the center (similar to our solar system). However, in contradistinction, the galaxy rotation curve remains flat. This discrepancy (allowing Kepler's laws) is resolved by concluding that the mass distribution in spiral galaxies is not similar to that of the solar system.

There is also the matter of volatility dispersions related to the measurement of mass distribution in elliptical galaxies or globular clusters. Ordinarily, velocity dispersion estimates of elliptical galaxies do not match the predicted velocity dispersion from the observed mass distribution. Then, the apparent way to resolve the discrepancy is to postulate the existence of non-luminous matter. Enter "dark matter."

The literature discusses other observational aspects of the "dark matter" hypothesis, including galaxy clusters, gravitational lensing, CMB, and others. The overwhelming evidence supports the observational conclusion that our empirical models of reality struggle to understand the function of universal, large-scale structures. We are apparently struggling with a hypothetical type of matter that seems to fit our empirical model of reality.

An Alternative Quantum Hypothesis

The scientific literature seems to indicate that the "dark matter" hypothesis favors the assumption that our space-time model of reality is an eternal concept. However, the observed behavioral patters of "dark matter" suggest powerful energy forces acting in particular regions of universal activities (black holes, galaxies, etc.). The question is: what is the source of that energy and why is it hypothesized as "dark matter"? Under these conditions, the "dark matter" hypothesis would negate the validity of our natural laws, particularly the laws of entropy.

Space-time was created. Matter is an output of that creation. Matter is an entropic (temporal) concept. Matter, of itself, is not capable of creation. However, it is necessary to mention a special case for matter that is related to universal sector regeneration (stars, galaxies) where matter is an active participant in that regeneration process. The process is described as the natural formation of black holes. (See my paper: "A Quantum Perspective on Black Holes"). The contribution of matter to this complex regeneration process is related to the direct influence of mass-energy that induces an interpretation of matter behavior considered to be unusual (non-emitting electromagnetic radiation) to its primary universal purpose.

From a hypothetical quantum perspective, mass is an eternal entity and is the physical energy generator in the whole of the Universe — including space-time. Mass provides the necessary energy to perpetuate a functionally efficient universal system.

There are no paradoxes in nature except those that are perceived through an unfocused lens of empirical reality models. As mentioned earlier, the observational evidence of energy activity from spiral galaxies is not similar to that of the solar system. In either case, there is a functional energy component in operation to accommodate both these natural conditions. Certainly, matter is present in any galaxy or solar system. The question is what function does matter provide in any particular universal sector operation. My quantum model would hypothesize that it is the natural function for mass-energy to operate and to maintain solar systems and galaxies throughout their respective normal entropic cycles. Mass is the quantum physical energy component available for the task. In contradistinction, matter, in a physical sense, is theoretically a created entity. Ignoring the complex aspects of cognition (metaphysical), matter provides the platform for solar systems and galaxy activities as an inert, passive function.

Understanding the relationship between entropic (empirical) and non-entropic (eternal) systems suggests the necessity to delineate what is meant by these specific entities. For instance, matter (entropic) and mass (eternal) are not the same thing. They are intimately related but do not reside in the same dimension. An attempt to describe "dark matter" as a non-entropic entity baffles the imagination. The "dark matter" hypothesis is related to a quantum energy perspective where its observation is fundamentally connected to an eternal perspective — particularly a mass-energy induced influence. Again, mass (eternal) and matter (entropic) are intimately related, but their purposes in the whole Universe represent specific and unique functions and operations.

Conclusion

From a quantum perspective, the "dark matter" hypothesis is a misnomer. The current modeling of cosmic structure formation (galaxies, solar systems), along with the anisotropies observed in the CMB, would indicate that a quantum interpretation of "dark matter," as specifically related to any functionally related activity in the Universe, would be instigated by mass-energy rather than by matter. In that sense, the observed behavior of this universal energy phenomenon we call "dark matter" obeys Kepler's laws, and mass would be the natural physical energy component for any universal sector-related operation.

As stated, mass and matter are unfortunately not clearly understood as separate entities which provide specific and differing universal functions. At issue here is the limitation of our space-time continuum model that describes only our empirical reality. For example, the concept of infinity actually operating in an entropic system is a physical absurdity. An entropic system is, by definition, finite in any interpretation of its universal creation. Matter (a created component) operates in our entropic system in a manner characterized by its inertness. Matter is functionally an inert entity. Contrarily, the concept of infinity belongs to the realm of an infinite eternal system (mass-motion) and to the immutable universal laws (metaphysical) of the calculus.

If it were simply physical mass that triggered the creation of space-time, whence comes energy? The essential aspects of this question are the eternal natural laws that govern the physical mass-energy operation of the whole Universe. In contrast, our created space-time continuum operates as a complex regeneration process. It is identified as a reproductive process in the sense that its temporal condition is described by the laws of entropy. This temporal reproductive activity is a generational function not to be construed as a creative activity. Matter, identified as a created entity, is not functionally capable of creation nor, by extension, is it capable of being the physical operating engine of the whole Universe. A particular function of matter is to provide the bodies and the platform on which the evolutionary development of its sentient creatures emerge from ego-consciousness toward greater conscious awareness.

Unfortunately, our empirical model of reality (space-time) has caused created inert matter to be included with eternal mass as the functional energy engine of the whole Universe.

Corresponence on Dark Matter with Larry Partain, Ph.D.,
Physicist, Translational Resarch Associates

Ken,

As usual, I read your latest blog on dark matter and your five-dimensional model with fascination. You really captured some of the awe and excitement from the recent detection of gravity waves with implied relationships to dark matter. I found that you are better informed on some of the subtle details of dark matter where I do not yet have an idea or opinion. I did particularly note your summary brief descriptions of multiple details of your model. However, none of this was placed into the basic language or science which is mathematics that can be objectively confirmed or falsified by some physical experiment or observation. In one place, you mentioned a decrease in entropy. For a closed system I am a strong believer that entropy must either stay the same or grow without the option of decreasing. Other than that, I just have to continue to think and wonder about what I really believe in the pioneering aspect of physics that rarely involves a real test — the LIGO results in a major contradiction of this last statement. Good luck on your continued development and evolution of your model as new breakthrough information continues at almost a snail's pace given its cosmological importance.

Larry

Larry,

Thanks for the feedback on the Laser Interferometer Gravitational Observatory (LIGO) experiment from my black holes paper. I have never been good at remembering acronyms. Anyway, LIGO did provide a useful tool supporting the scientific investigation of black holes.

In my models, the laws of thermodynamic entropy are immutable (the measure of disorder in an entropic system) requiring that any energy disorder cannot decrease. We could not agree more! However, the question of entropy in the region of black holes is complicated. The laws of entropy apply to our created space-time continuum world. Mass-motion is an eternal system. Entropy has no functional activity in that system. You might say that the energy quotient in an eternal system is a constant. From my paper on black holes, the eternal mass-energy provided in the universal sector regenerational process (the quantum quotient) overcomes the increase of entropy of a dying star (entropy provided by the presence of collapsing matter). The instantaneous effect is a mass-energy transfer that makes itself an initial, entropic decrease. This action activates a new entropic system (galaxy) that is the outcome of the complex (mass-energy plus matter) super-nova reseeding process.

Your questions are always welcome.

Kenneth

The Science of Infinity

Introduction

Infinity is a concept. It belongs to a realm beyond the empirical. The extraordinary attempts to qualify/quantify infinity have only succeeded in chasing us around in circles describing myriad definitions for the concept of infinity. Negative infinity, infinite set theory, metaphysical infinity, infinitely large or infinitely small, and on and on. All these concepts have been exhaustingly explored and summed up by Max Tegmarks' comment: "Infinity is a beautiful concept — and it is ruining physics."

In light of this apparent crisis in physics, it becomes necessary to consider and explore infinity in a perspective beyond the empirical.

The Definition Of Infinity

For the purposes of this paper, infinity is defined as a concept describing something without any bound or something larger than any natural number. A concept that theoretically exists in nature. An idea of something without end — beyond empirical measurement.

The Limits of Infinity in Our Created Empirical World

By definition, our created world is not boundless. Any physical, created entity (matter) is measurable since that is a functional property of matter in empirical reality. The essential condition or element that could support the existence of infinity in our space-time world is negated by the creation process along with the functional operation of matter in empirical reality. It is important to note that matter was not only created but is temporal in nature. Matter has no place or function in any universal system beyond the empirical.

As an example, the speed of light is a measurable entity that is useful in explaining the limits of a relative infinity in our empirical world. From the special theory of relativity, matter and time would cease to exist at the speed of light. Matter would, in fact, become light itself. Paradoxically, its wave function would arguably transform into a particle function. Hypothetically, matter and time are measurable parameters within the context of a created, entropic system and are by definition not infinite. Their limited operational functions would no longer be relevant to the purpose for which they were created.

Hypothetically, anything that has been created becomes, by definition, an empirical concept. Further, any creation event can be measured within the realm of that particular event. Its corollary logically requires that any creation event must be preceded by a realm beyond its empirical creation — arguably related in intent and perspective. The nature of things in any realm (empirical or eternal) follow the laws of a natural process defined by orderly operations dependent on their particular functions. As stated, it is axiomatic that any created entity can be circumscribed by empirical methods. Translating this sense of logic, our empirical world is not functionally or dimensionally capable of a reality encompassing infinity.

The fundamental inviolable pillars of western scientific understanding are that our empirical world was created and that this created system is entropic — temporal in nature. From this perspective, the only conceivable reason that the idea of infinity as a plausible entity in the "whole" of reality must be related to our cognitive awakening to the idea of a realm beyond the sensate — the realm that created our empirical world. The idea of infinity must have arisen from our gift of cognition offered to us in the creation process, reflecting an awareness of the nature of things and the operational behavior of natural processes within an orderly, universal system. This natural cognitive perception (the psyche) is struggling to establish a relationship between the eternal and the infinite — that these concepts co-exist. We can, at least, articulate the idea of infinity in some expansive sense of reality, perhaps through the auspices of mathematics describing the infinite in relation to the eternal.

The Eternal and the Infinite

The eternal defines the infinite. The characterization of one encompasses the other — as they are intricately related. They belong to the same realm of reality. They pre-exist our created, empirical world. In that functional context, our empirical world is cognitively connected by the idea (concept) of the eternal and the infinite. Logically, our empirical world is directly and ultimately related to the creation event that produced it.

The question of whether we can relate to the idea of understanding the concept of infinity in any physical or metaphysical sense must include the tools available to us in that process. The process is daunting. The prospect of investigating a boundless entity (infinity) in a created, empirical world is a contradiction in terms. However, if we were able to initiate an investigation process beyond our created system to the creation itself (its eternal process) — the question of the efficacy of an infinite realm is theoretically feasible.

In a metaphysical sense, infinity is related to our gift of cognition and potentially relatable to mathematics. It is hypothetically possible to explore (not measure) infinity from the calculus since it is an eternal operating entity in the whole of reality. Through the auspices of the creation process, the calculus is universally available to us with reference to the eternal system in which it resides. A realm, dimensionally separate, but related to the empirical.

In concert with the availability of the calculus, our gift of cognition has connected us to the idea of an infinite realm present in the whole of reality. The creation process has provided us with the natural laws that could hypothetically link an understanding of our created world to the creation event.

From a physical perspective, it is possible to explore the concept of infinity through a model that recognizes the eternal entities of mass and motion and precludes the temporal entities of matter and time. Utilizing these separate dimensional relationships between eternal and entropic systems is critical to a perspective toward understanding infinity.

In this perspective, any investigative approach to the efficacy of the infinite from a physical perspective must include eternal entities. Unfortunately, since matter (empirical) and mass (eternal) are considered basically the same (large and small), rather than related entities in different dimensions, a physical approach to understanding the concept of infinity is impossible. (See my paper "A Five-Dimensional Model of the Universe.")

Conclusion

A physical interpretation of infinity awaits a new quantum model of reality beyond classical physics.

Presently, the idea of infinity resides in the psyche as part of the instinctual process we call cognition — the gift to us from the creation process. It represents a glimpse of the whole of reality, shrouded in a veil of possibilities and wonder.

Correspondence on Science of Infinity with Larry Partain, Ph.D., Physicist

Ken,

As always it is refreshingly intriguing for me to read through your blogs which actually stimulate me to think well beyond my usual norms. This is the case for your recent blog on infinity and science. My first recollection on infinity is from the science of differential equations where the derivative of $y = f(x)$ of an ever increasing curvature gives a slope s that is equal to Dy divided by Dx in the limit as Dx goes to zero. However as Dx goes to zero, there are an infinite number of slope values s as x goes from zero to one or between any other two related numbers. I think Newton was the first to develop this calculus that led to differential equations needed for his breakthrough Laws of Motion. Calculus as well as continuously varying slopes from its mathematics are just totally abstract concepts that are of immensely practical physical significance that fostered great leaps in amazing advancements in our modern world and civilization. However in a more recent vein I think of the wave/particle duality of light. I can calculate the current of any point in time from a solar cell by considering each photon "particle" and the rate at which they strike a solar cell when I multiply this by the quantum efficiency of a solar cell as I describe in my book on Solar Cells and their Applications. However to get the voltage of a solar cell I have to consider the continuous quantum wave electron properties inside a semiconductor like silicon to get the density of electronic states that limits solar cell voltage. This only gets weirder when I consider that photons traveling at the speed of light, at which point time ceases to advance, according to special relativity. The light photons detected by the Hubble Telescope from almost the 13 billion years back to the big bang, are apparently still from the billions of years time ago when they "now?" reach us, whatever that means.

I am beginning to wonder if true or false has any other purpose than philosophical comfort, with value only realized by how many useful practical things can be obtained given our present state of scientific advancement.

Larry

Larry,

Thank you for your email.

In an absolute sense, true and false must belong to the philosophical if the bases for true and false rest on limited models of reality. The empirical world (space-time) is an absolute physical reality, and the benefits from applying scientific knowledge (experimentation) to this empirical world cannot be underestimated. On the pillars of these empirical investigations the quantum world is borne and a new scientific world is glacially emerging from its roots. There is no "false" in the full realization of the creation process.

Since "the calculus" is an eternal, natural law, it contains within its whole structure the realization of the concept of infinity — practical or otherwise.

The wave/particle duality of light is more complex because it refers to the wave function (matter) and the particle function (mass). Their respective operational functions are different and they reside in different dimensions. Matter (empirical) behaves as a wave function and its velocity is limited to the speed of light (it becomes light at that velocity). Its speed is not infinite unless you want to call the speed of light infinite. Mass (eternal) has a different function in the operation of the whole of reality — empirical and eternal.

I believe our models of the physical world are ready and fully capable of investigations beyond empirical reality.

Kenneth

The Relationship Between Mass and Matter

Introduction

My fifth-dimensional model of reality hypothesizes that mass and matter are individually distinct entities. They are relativistically inter-related through a process of implicit derivation (a change of state/dimension) initiated by the Creator. (See my "Creator Model".) Matter is derived from mass and is a three-dimensional, empirical entity in our space-time continuum. Mass resides in the fifth dimension and is the eternal, physical engine component of the Creator's "Whole."

This paper attempts to explain the relationship between mass and matter as they function in my five-dimensional model of reality.

A Characteristic of Mass Relative to Matter

To understand more fully the complex relationship between mass and matter, it is useful to introduce the ideas of Chaos Theory. The scientific literature tells us that Chaos Theory is a study in non-linear dynamics, in which seemingly random events are actually predictable. In a scientific sense, the word chaos has a different meaning from its general usage as a state of confusion, lacking any order. Chaos Theory, which was discovered by physicist Henri Poincare, refers only to an "apparent" lack of order that always obeys particular natural laws. It represents a dynamic instability in certain physical systems. The two main components of Chaos Theory are:

- Physical systems, regardless of complexity, rely on an underlying natural order.
- Simple systems and events can cause complex behaviors and events. These occurrences are usually understood as sensitive dependence on initial conditions, and attributed to Edward Lorenz.

In contradistinction, Newtonian (space-time continuum) laws of physics are completely deterministic. The assumption is that perfect predictions of any physical system, in theory, is determined by the precision of the initial measurements in any particular experiment.

In a practical, empirical sense, this Newtonian concept is perfectly valid. However, in terms of Chaos Theory, the "apparent" lack of order in a system applies to particle (sub-atomic) behavior. Then, the issue becomes a question of whether mass (sub-atomic theory) and matter (wave theory) are fundamentally the same and whether these entities reside in the same dimension.

My five-dimensional model of the Universe hypothesizes that mass and matter, while indivisibly related, are not the same and that the two entities reside in different dimensions. The behavioral patterns of mass and matter — while related to fundamental laws of nature — have different and unique functions and objectives. Mass is the physical entity (component) of the Creator's "Whole" and is the energy engine of the entire Universe. Matter is the implicit derivative of mass and is the physical creation of our empirical space-time continuum, as part of the Creator's plan.

The whole of the Universe (five dimensions) is not, in any sense, chaotic. In a fifth-dimensional sense, mass is an eternal concept subject to natural laws and operating as a fully efficient entity. Matter (three-dimensional) is not chaotic, but operates in our space-time continuum as a temporal, entropic entity, governed by the Creator's natural laws.

Mass

Mass is a fifth-dimensional entity. It is the physical component (entity) of all Universal reality. Mass does not reside in our space-time continuum except as an implicit integral of matter. Mass, while directly related to matter and, by extension, to empirical kinetic energy, is not constrained by the natural laws of matter. Mass and matter and are not transposable entities.

Mass is not an empirical concept. It is a fifth-dimensional concept that functions to provide the physical energy to create, operate, and renew our empirical space-time continuum sense of reality.

Mass is not an entropic entity. It is an eternal concept and is the physical component of the Creator's "Whole," the Creator's unity comprising physical and metaphysical (the immutable laws of nature) components of Universal reality.

Matter

Matter is the implicit derivative of mass in our empirical space-time continuum sense of reality.

In my five-dimensional model of the Universe, mass and matter are separate entities where mass (an eternal concept) resides in the fifth dimension and matter (a temporal concept) is a relativistic entity in space-time. Matter does not exist in the fifth dimension.

The Universe is a mass/motion concept that has been implicitly derived into our space-time continuum. My model hypothesizes this derivation process as the whole of reality. Mass is an eternal concept in all of reality. Matter is a temporal entity, encompassing space-time. Matter is a three-dimensional concept in a time-related, empirical sense of reality. Its space-time environment is derived from mass and always operates with the boundaries of our space-time continuum's natural laws in our entropic envelope of empirical reality.

Matter performs this function of empirical reality as a consequence of the Creator's plan for a temporal evolution of sentient consciousness toward a higher level of consciousness beyond the ego structure. (See my papers on "The Creator Model" and "The Creator's Plan").

Matter is the empirical physical output of the Creator's plan. It is the physical "building block," the framework for the advent of sentient, cognitive conditions and their evolution.

Conclusion

An understanding of mass and matter, in relation to their indivisible functions, provides the critical elements necessary to understanding the physical aspects of Universal reality. Further, an understanding of these physical entities will provide the framework for connecting physical reality to the natural laws of the Universe (metaphysical) and to those respective operations.

The whole of the Universe is not a confused, disordered entity. It is a mass/motion, matter/time concept intricately woven into a natural process of physical and metaphysical order for the purpose of its related, cognitive evolution.

Correspondence on the Relationship Between Mass and Matter with Larry Staples, Jungian Analyst

Ken,

I've read your paper several times. It seems to me you are building step by step toward something spiritual. At first, I thought your building had a scientific goal. Now I'm beginning to feel the goal is primarily spiritual and that the final structure, when it is entirely built, will be much more spiritual than scientific. I may be wrong, but it seems to me that, like Alchemy, the science actually conceals a spritual, scientific quest that is taking place beneath the cover of a discipline that tends to be more intellectually respectable in Western rationalism. I may be wrong and admit I have come to this conclusion for the reason that I don't really understand the science. It seems incidental to a broader purpose. It seems to me that each of these pieces somehow reflects a part of yourself and adds to the broader picture.

Larry

Larry,

Thank you for your comments on my paper.

My fundamental hypotheses are my two models — the Creator and the Five-Dimensional Universe. They are my beacons for discovery. Without them, I am lost in a sea of images and projections.

Your question regarding spirituality has dogged me all through my life. My Creator model envisions the Creator as an eternal "Unity" in a mandala (seed) comprising two fundamental components — a physical component (mass) and a metaphysical component (natural laws) —which govern the whole of reality.

Spirituality is not a wholly metaphysical construct. It is an integral part of the Creator's "Whole." It is manifest in the immutable natural laws of the Universe and is indivisibly linked to the physical world — the mass (energy) component.

Science, the theoretical explanation of natural phenomena (my preferred definition), cannot be divisible from the concept of spirituality. The essence (perhaps the whole) of our reality is the creation process itself, and that ultimately leads us to the Creator.

Yes, my goal seems to be primarily headed in the spiritual realm because the Creator created what we call our space-time continuum for a purpose. The creation was not a random event. Not only are we considering a consciousness beyond the ego, but along with its higher consciousness are the extraordinary eternal natural laws that govern the Universe, operating through a physical energy (mass).

Kenneth

Ken,

You are making your journey along the scientific path with which you feel most knowledgable and comfortable. Since we have to make bold assumptions and leaps of faith to get to the entity we know as "God" — whether "God" turns out to be a wave, a string, a sub-sub-sub-atomic particle or the evolutionary tendency — I doubt it makes any difference whether we enter the journey through art, religion, or science. So, why not enter the search along an avenue that is familiar and comfortable to one's self.

Since "God" is unprovable, we can only arrive there by making bold assumptions and taking huge leaps of faith to traverse the chasm between the known and the unknown. Something unknown always lies behind our last discovery. Behind matter is the molecule; behind the molecule is the atom; and behind the atom are the elemental particles we can never grasp. I've made it much simpler for myself by just assuming there is something that creates and sustains all that there is. It makes my journey short, inelegant, and extremely unsophisticated. While I am unable to follow the more complex and breathtakingly sinuous paths, I nevertheless appreciate them and envy them, except for the hard work involved.

And here's the kicker. The end of all my foreshortened explorations is to find that "God" is a beach. Watch out for too many hours in the lab.

Larry

Larry,

Thank you. I will be careful about too many hours in the lab. Also you may be right that "Gods" are a beach.

Allow me one small prerogative. I cannot argue the concept of "Gods" in relation to the Creator. "Gods" are unknowable (unprovable) because they are projections from the collective unconscious. They represent an instinctual concept that is fundamentally metaphysical in their construct. They are gifts from the Creator to an awakening cognitive process in humankind.

In contradistinction, the Creator is a universal concept. The Creator created the whole of our empirical world, including the ecological space-ship we call earth, for a purpose. This creation process is both physical and metaphysical. The truth of of that is to be found in nature and in cognition (at a level beyond ego). I believe it is part of the Creator's plan for us to discover.

We are products of the creation process and, in that sense, we are endowed with an essence of the Creator's nature and with an introduction to the Creator's level of consciousness. I have no illusions that this level of consciousness will ever find me — for it is a long journey of discovery. Somehow, it has become my process.

Kenneth

Ken,

You are definitely on a path of discovery. And I applaud you for your efforts. In some ways, it would be just easier to sit around and rock.

From your last email, it seems it is important to your model and system of thought to make a distinction between "Creator" and "God." Fortunately, in these matters we are free to make whatever assumptions we need to make to arrive at constructs we are comfortable with. Certainly, the assumption that "Creator" and "God" are different concepts is quite unconventional. In most languages even, the words are interchangeable. But I find your assumption as interesting as the conventional one or any others I've heard and can see why that distinction is necessary to your ideas about the fifth dimension. It does seem to me that anything that is unknown and unknowable, like concepts of "Creator" or "God," has to be a projection from the unconscious. But so what? Who knows where your discoveries will lead you.

Larry

Larry,

Thank you for your comments on the distinction between "Creator" and "Gods." Yes, it seems that these concepts are projections from the unconscious. However, the roots of these projections are coming from different levels of the sphere of the unconscious. Your comments will help me focus attention upon further review of my Creator model and the Creator's plan regarding our relationship to unconscious projections and purposes.

Kenneth

The Concept of Mass

The special theory of relativity defines the energy-mass relationship as one and the same. Energy is mass and mass is energy. This relationship is simply stated as follows:

$$E=mc2$$

where c is the velocity of light (a constant).

The equation becomes more complicated when relativistic mass and rest mass are considered and where velocities close to the speed of light (the constant c) are introduced. The full form of the equation becomes:

$$E = mc2 = moc2 \text{ / divided by the square root of } 1 - v2/c2$$

for any non-stationary body. The relativistic nature of mass (it increases as velocity increases), along with the complex "relativisitic kinetic energy" inherent in this mathematical relationship, further complicate this simple formal expression for an equivalent energy-mass interpretation.

Before we begin to consider the concept of mass as an entity unto itself, it is necessary to understand the derivation of Einstein's equation using the formal calculus method.

Two important factors are introduced in the calculus derivation of E=mc2.

First, that energy is the integral of force (F) with respect to distance (S). Kinetic energy is defined as:

K = the integral (from o to s) of Fds

Second, the introduction of Newton's second law of motion where force (F) can be shown as:

$$F = \frac{d(mv)}{dt}$$

Then, the equation for kinetic energy becomes:

K = the integral (from o to s) of $\frac{d(mv)}{dt}$ ds

The solution to this equation is available in the literature and is integrated by parts to yield a complex result in a more simplified form:

E = Relativistic kinetic energy + mc2

To simplify the equation further, the speed of (i.e., the relativistic kinetic energy component) the particle is set to zero, and the equation becomes:

E=mc2

While it is scientifically believed that mass and energy are the same thing (certainly in an empirical sense), the formal calculus solution included a complicated relativistic kinetic energy factor (a particle factor) that was conveniently removed from the equation by assuming the speed of relativisitic particles to be zero. Also, this mathematical exercise in defining the relationship between energy and mass precludes an understanding of what energy and mass as separate entities are.

The Einstein model did not define either mass or energy, but rather implicitly introduced the mathematical relationship between the two entities as if they were equal and the same. However, these relationships were introduced in mathematical terms to explore not only the physical relationship between energy and mass but also its relativistic nature. In fact, Einstein was troubled by how and why energy was released from mass and was skeptical that the transfer could ever be done. He was satisfied that his equation was empirically consistent, and the model does predict what happens to bodies moving at high speeds in our space-time continuum.

What Is Mass?

My fifth-dimensional model of the Universe hypothesizes the expansion of our present four-dimensional space-time continuum model. The space-time model cannot adequately interpret data from fifth-dimensional products (sub-atomic particles) as scientific study progresses from empirical constructs to the new reality of a more complex five-dimensional Universe.

My five-dimensional model hypothesizes that mass becomes a relational component of energy (physical) and is implicitly relational to the derivative of mass into matter. Mass is not an empirical concept. It is not a space-time continuum (four-dimensional) entity. Mass cannot be fully understood in terms of its relativistic relationship to the integral of force over distance (i.e., energy).

Mass is a fifth-dimensional entity. Mass is the physical component (entity) of all Universal reality. It does not reside in our space-time continuum except as an implicit integral of matter. Matter is implicitly derived from mass.

Mass, while it is directly relational to matter and, by extension, to empirical kinetic energy, is not constrained by the natural laws of matter. Mass and matter are not transposable entitles. Mass particle speeds are not limited by the velocity of light and may approach infinite velocities. The speed of light as an infinite concept is an empirical construct.

Mass and matter exist in different relational states (dimensions) of reality. They are no more the same thing than energy is the same thing as mass — allowing there is a relational aspect to the two entities as described above in the formal calculus method.

Conclusion

The Einstein model did not define either mass or energy but implicitly introduced the mathematical relationship between the two entities as if they were equal and the same.

Mass is an eternal, Universal entity. My fifth-dimensional model of the Universe hypothesizes that the fundamental elements of mass particles cannot attain a velocity of zero, and that the relativistic kinetic energy factor in the calculus solution for mass/energy cannot be eliminated. Mass particles are capable of speeds beyond the speed of light — to potentially infinite velocities. As stated, mass is the physical component of all Universal reality. Mass is the physical entity that perpetuates the ebb and flow — the cycles of our finite Universe.

Mass and motion are inextricably linked entities that are relational to matter and time. My next paper will endeavor to expand the relationship between motion and time and connect these functions to space-time and the fifth dimension.

A Physical "Unit" of a Single Dimension

Introduction

In the study of three-dimension geometry, the analysis is usually treated as a spatial coordinate system of interactive planes (x,y,z). They are treated as the nature of space and, in that sense, they are inextricably linked one to the other. However, it is generally convenient to simplify a particular problem as a planar concept (two-dimensional) or as a line (one-dimensional); but the fundamental spatial reality of its created construct is always interactively three-dimensional.

The practical use of a spatial coordinate system of interactive planes can lead to certain misinterpretations of length, width, and depth — as if they were interchangeable dimensions depending on specific reference criteria.

Our natural spatial reality (three-dimensions) differentiates each dimension as a separate entity even though all are inextricably linked. There would never be a natural misinterpretation of the particular function of one dimension vis-a-vis the others. For purposes of empirical geometrical operation, what we call our constructed, spatial coordinate system (x,y,z) is not translatable to a greater understanding of my hypothetical five-dimensional model of reality and of nature itself.

This paper seeks to determine the existence of a physical "unit" of a single dimension in any concept of reality. This physical "unit" is also postulated as a concept that is indivisible unto itself.

Is the idea of a "unit" of a single, dimension simply an illusion, or is it a hypothetical possibility in any sense of reality? Have we simply conditioned ourselves into accepting the concept of a coordinate system as a physical function of reality? Certainly this visual impression is fundamental to our understanding and development of empirical reality.

Again, the question is whether a "unit" of a single dimension actually exists in any concept of physical reality, or whether we are confined within the prospect of an interpretation of unitary dimensional reality based on mathematical language (metaphysical) in keeping with Universal natural laws.

Dimensions in Our Space-Time Continuum Model

In a four-dimensional model (space-time continuum) of reality, there are no such things as space and time. Only space-time. Space-time is a continuum. The special theory of relativity hypothesizes that the parts of the continuum cannot be broken down into separate dimensions. There are no breaks in space-time; they flow continuously. According to the theory, we live, breathe, and exist in a four-dimensional space-time continuum. We live in an empirical world where:

- Space and time are related in an intimate, indivisible manner.
- The "fourth dimension" is a mathematical construct and is a translation from one language to another. The original language is mathematics and the other is

English. The problem is that there is no way to precisely express in translation what the mathematical language says. Time as the fourth dimension is a label we give to a relationship. The relationship in question is the relationship between space and time as it is expressed mathematically in the special theory of relativity. It is useful and convenient for physicists to expound on this four-dimensional model for experimental purposes and to study empirical reality.

As our empirical sensors progress, the space-time continuum model becomes complicated. For example, a one-dimensional continuum (in a space-time model) is a line. Theoretically, we would say that the line is a series of points with the points infinitely close to each other. Therefore, the line flows continuously from one end to the other. A two-dimensional continuum is the wall. All the points on the wall are in contact, and the wall is a continuous surface. A three-dimensional continuum is what we call space. This space concept is our observable physical reality. However, our space-time sense of reality is compromised by referring to our three-dimensional (space) as a coordinate system. In effect, we have devised a technique that allows us to imagine that dimensions are divisible. We approximate reality by using the term "spatial coordinate system." This coordinate system is effectively used as a vehicle for convenience and simplification in molding our empirical world through a process of mathematical approximations. The scientific results from this effort cannot be overstated, but it does not answer the question of whether a "unit" of a single dimension exists in space-time reality or, in fact, whether such a "unit" has any significance in any sense of reality.

The concept of matter (space) is fundamentally structural in its function and operation. The creation of organic and inorganic matter, as it particularly relates to the complex ecosystem we call Earth, should be understood in reference to how perfectly suited we are to our environment. We are endowed with the complete natural system we need to carry out the purpose of our creation.

What is being postulated here is that the functions of matter (space) do not require or necessitate the divisibility of spatial dimensions. The natural laws that govern the Universe are immutable, eternal, and efficient in their operations. There is no apparent purpose or function for matter to require the divisibility of dimensions in a space-time continuum sense. At this point, it is necessary to consider other possibilities for a physical "unit" of a single dimension. This necessity leads us to the consideration of mass as providing the functional purpose for the divisibility of dimensions on the basis of the necessity for the operation, propagation, and regeneration of the Universe.

Before we move on to the discussion of mass, it is appropriate to consider the purpose for which the creation process introduced matter (space) in the Universe. What is the purpose of matter and what is its function? For our hypothetical purposes here, the crucial issue involves the primary functions of matter and by extension the function of mass. (For a more detailed analysis of mass/matter functions, see my papers on "The Creator" and "The Creator's Plan"). For our discussion here, suffice it to say that the function of matter is to provide sustenance for its organic posterity and for its organic systems to evolve.

Hypothesis for a "Unit" of a Single Dimension

Our search must lead us away from the idea of matter as the single dimensional "unit" solution, and towards the physical concept of mass, operating in conjunction with its natural Universal functions, providing an answer.

Our space-time continuum model of reality does include a concept of mass, but it is not distinguishable from matter (certainly in a dimensional sense), even though its mass relationship is fundamentally an energy-related concept (in space-time). However, while mass and matter are intimately related (see my paper, "The Relationship Between Mass and Matter"), they are separate entities operating in different dimensions.

It then becomes necessary to understand the function of mass if our hypothesis for a physical "unit" of a single dimension can be considered. Mass is not an empirical concept. It is a fifth-dimensional concept that functions to provide the physical energy to create, operate, and renew our empirical space-time continuum. Mass is a fifth-dimensional entity. It is the physical component of all Universal reality. Mass, while directly related to matter, is not constrained by the laws of matter. Mass and matter are not transposable entities.

Discussion for a "Unit" of a Single Dimension

My hypothesis is rooted in the idea that the eternal natural laws of the Universe are operationally focused toward specific tasks and functions. These natural laws operate in a totally efficient manner to carry out specific needs of the Universe. The physical vehicle for Universal operational functions is mass.

My hypothesis proceeds to the question of how and why the Universe can possibly function/operate within the constraint that the speed of light is infinite (it is infinite in our space-time model). The hypothetical answer is that the speed of light is not infinite and that superluminal velocities are attained in the mass structure. It is crucial to make this point because the validity of a physical unit of a single dimension rests on the functional requirement of a singular dimension to carry out operations within the whole of the Universe (beyond consideration of "local causes").

To proceed, it is necessary to introduce the idea of Max Planck's experimentally proven concept called the Quantum of Action. It is expressed mathematically as:

$$E=hv, \text{ where}$$
$$v=\text{frequency,}$$
$$h=\text{Planck's constant,}$$
$$E=\text{electromagnetic energy.}$$

Planck's Quantum of Action is the bedrock of quantum physics and explains that all material systems (physical) can absorb or give off electromagnetic energy only in chunks (quanta). The statistical predictions of quantum theory have always been proven correct.

As stated above, there is no purpose or function for matter (three-dimensional) to need or require a transformation to a single dimension. Matter always operates within the limits of its natural functions. Mass has no such limitations. Its function and purpose is to operate and perpetuate the Universe. Mass is not subject to the laws of matter and is capable of transformations beyond dimensions and infinite velocities (motion) beyond the speed of light.

The idea of superluminal velocities is inextricably woven within the natural law argument for "connectivity" throughout the Universe. Dr. J.S. Bell suggested the mathematical theory that the separate parts of the Universe are connected in a distinct, fundamental, and immediate way.

In conjunction with this "connectivity" concept, it becomes appropriate to introduce two theories on superluminal velocities operational in the Universe.

First is the Tachyon Theory proposed by physicists A. Summerfeld and G. Feinberg. Briefly, tachyons are theoretical particles (fifth-dimensional products) capable of superluminal speeds. They require the transfer of energy and have "real mass." However, tachyons are "wave functions" that satisfy a wave equation. When tachyons lose energy, they gain speed. When they gain energy, they slow down. The slowest speed for tachyons is the speed of light.

Second is Jack Sarfatti's theory on "Superluminal Transfer of Negentropy Without Signals." The major point of Sarfatti's theory is that any quantum jump is a space-like superluminal transfer of negentropy. (Negentropy is a measure of order — negative entropy.) Also, there is no transport of energy — nothing travels between Area A and Area B. There is, however, an instantaneous change in the quality of the energy in both Areas A and B. The theory suggests a communications transfer.

Theoretically, Scarfatti's theory can be derived from the indivisibility of Planck's Quantum of Action, implying that quantum jumps between states must be discrete. A quantum system does not pass through a continuous series of intermediate states in any observable change.

In contradistinction, an issue with Tachyon theory is that tachyons are theoretical particles that operate as wave functions and satisfy wave equations. Since mass is the operative physical entity under consideration (see my paper "A

Five-Dimensional Model of the Universe"), then its function requires a transformation to particle/wave states to carry out certain superluminal Universal requirements.

My model hypothesizes that mass always operates in the fifth dimension and its particular function determines its transformative state — particle or wave. Also, mass is the physical component of the Universe — that is, related but not dependent — on time. Motion is the instigator of mass action.

The question of whether a "unit" of a single dimension exists in any physical reality is dependent on the functional requirement for the Universe to exist and to perpetuate itself. The idea for Universal "connectivity" in conjunction with superluminal velocities would argue for a transformative mass entity to provide the "communications" link.

Conclusion

The indivisibility of three-dimensional matter (space) requires us to project and to conceptualize a physical "unit" of a single dimension beyond our spatial coordinate system. This practical, devised coordinate system, considered as a learned projection, presents us with an intellectual conundrum. It introduces the idea of why the nature of any reality would require or necessitate a specific one-dimensional "unit" entity for its operation and purposes.

In this case, Tachyon Theory and Scarfatti's non-transfer of quantum energy without signals are not directly translatable ideas to our space-time continuum model of reality. Space-time is an entropic system and time is a temporal entity derived from external motion. However, Tachyon Theory and Scarfatti's theory are translatable to my five-dimensional model of the Universe. Both theories recognize the Universal need for superluminal velocities and imply that mass is the physical operative for this functional application.

Planck's Quantum of Action does not necessarily require the transfer of energy (in this instance, Tachyon Theory is not applicable). Therefore, mass (for superluminal velocities) can theoretically be transformed into a "physical wave" construct. However, the Quantum of Action is a particle phenomenon. In my model, its particle function operates as a fifth-dimensional entity beyond the limits of space-time.

The physical "unit" of a single dimension hypothesis rests on the supposition that mass is a transformative entity (particle, wave, or dimension) dependent on its particular function, operation, or Universal application.

In contradistinction, the speed of light is infinite in our space-time continuum. At the speed of light, matter (space) is transformed into light. It becomes the final essence of wave phenomena. This transformative process is a fundamental condition of empirical reality and is not simply translatable to dimensional analysis. However, mass is an eternal entity that resides in a dimension beyond our space-time continuum (the fifth dimension) and is not limited by the speed of light. Mass is the physical "whole" of the "connected" Universal system.

The properties of mass are transformative into any change of state (particle, wave, dimension) depending on the particular Universal function. The operative catalyst for this transformation process is the eternal calculus.

The Void Concept

Introduction

From an empirical scientific space-time continuum (four-dimensional) sense of reality, the concept of a universal void is a physical impossibility.

However, my models of the fifth dimension and the Creator theorize that our space-time continuum Universe was created from the fifth dimension. The models further imply that the Creator resides in the fifth dimension and has existed throughout all eternity (a perpetual state) and that the energies (physical and metaphysical) integral to the Creator's dualism created our space-time Universe through a process of implicit derivation (the eternal calculus). In effect, our space-time continuum is a derivative from the Creator's fifth-dimensional whole. The fifth-dimensional products of mass-motion are differentiated into matter-time entities.

My models, per se, neither prove nor disprove the concept of a Universal void, but they do introduce the question of whether the dualistic nature of the Creator is eternal in the Universe. To consider whether the dualistic nature of the Creator is eternal, one approach is to suggest its antithesis — the Universal void. The void concept then becomes an exercise in an abstract proposition.

An Exercise In An Abstract Proposition

Consider the concept of a void — where apparently nothing exists. A void without the Creator and without the Universe — a vacuum.

However, if you objectify the concept of a void, that is, if you externalize its presence, then, hypothetically, the void must represent a particular "condition," i.e., a nascent state of reality. In a logical sequence, the void becomes a proposition upon which another proposition depends — the antecedent of this "condition" proposition. The antecedent of this proposition must be a metaphysical concept or construct since any physical concept would be inconsistent with the definition of a void. In fact, the only prospect or possibility of the concept of existence would be comprised of a latent tendency — a "condition." Assuming this "condition" possibility, it may be argued philosophically that any condition — including a void — has a tension component. The void — by definition — is hypothetically a "condition." It is an option of probability. The void may be considered a condition that requires energy to sustain its presence. In that sense, a tension would exist in that particular "condition" and its essence would be metaphysical. Then the "condition" (the void) can exist with only a metaphysical component — a metaphysical tendency. The presence of its condition demands a metaphysical interpretation. We are then confronted with a conclusion that the physical component of any reality must be generated out of a metaphysical condition.

As stated, while we are empirically aware that our space-time continuum exists, it is arguably regenerative (on a solar/galactic basis) and requires energy to sustain its finite existence. In fact, empirical space-time represents a conditional reality, no more or less a "condition" than that of a void. Also, that no conceptual "condition" (void) preceded this apparent reality.

The Void Conundrum

Can something be created from nothing — a void? Conceptually, the possibility of such an occurrence is anathema to any perspective or any condition of conscious, empirical reality. We are fortunate to have the necessary empirical data that describe our created space-time continuum — and that data base is the foundation of any complete understanding of Universal reality. Our present empirical data would suggest that the concept of a Universal void (in an absolute sense) is an impossibility.

It is here theoretically proposed that any form or concept of Universal reality — including a void — must require a "conditional" process to sustain it. In that sense, some form of reality has always existed in a perpetual process — and in a dimension beyond entropic considerations. A question is whether this pre-existing "condition" is a physical or metaphysical process or both. Also, whether the Creator has always existed (infinitely perpetual) or was the Creator created out of some pre-existent "condition." And if so, was the essence of that condition physical and/or metaphysical. The idea of the "condition" being both physical and metaphysical would suggest that the Creator always existed in its model form (see "The Creator") — albeit conditionally. Assuming that to be the case, then the concept of the void would be conditionally disproved. We are then left with either a physical or metaphysical "condition" to explain Universal reality or to assume a Creator in perpetuity.

The void is a conundrum because it specifically requires that a physical condition (and its attendant physical energy) must be created out of a metaphysical concept/construct. The Creator's model is both a physical and metaphysical entity — a dualism. Either we are considering a "condition" (a void) that preceded the Creator, or the process by which the Creator model evolved.

As complex as that situation presents itself, we are left with the prospect of understanding the creation process. We are approaching a cognitive level of extreme psychological inflation since we are the "created" and not the Creator.

All of this said — the models suggest that we must persist here. The hypothesis is that any reality must be constituted as a "condition" and that any "condition" requires energy to sustain its reality and its present function. Also, its reality and its function are subject to change.

The question then becomes one of whether the void, by definition, must contain a metaphysical component if it is, in fact, a "condition" of reality. If we assume that the hypothesis cannot claim that the void is a "condition" of reality, then the question is moot and the argument is circular. However, granting that the void is a "condition," then the antecedent of that hypothetical proposition must be a metaphysical construct. Then, the salient principle of the void is that its presence is metaphysical in concept. Also, the void must constitute a particular state — a "condition" (an apparent stasis). Then, from this premise, any sense of physical reality is derived from metaphysical energy. What we describe as a physical entity (matter) has been hypothetically derived from metaphysical energy and/or a metaphysical condition (a state or dimension).

The "condition" argument for the Universal void concept certainly challenges the empirical structure of science as it would any hypothetical model of reality. In this perspective, we are required to proceed a priori in establishing a hypothesis for any sense of our known Universal construct or, in fact, any sense of reality. How did we get from a hypothetical void "condition" to the Universal "condition" we experience now as space-time. Did a void ever exist or is the Creator of the Universe an eternal concept?

The arguments against a Universal void are strong since the void hypothesis represents a "condition" that would require energy to sustain its "condition." By definition, that energy cannot be physical or physically generated. From this perspective, the concept of a Universal void is an untenable proposition because something always existed, whether it be physical or metaphysical in its structure. Another question is whether something physical always existed. Matter has not always existed. Matter was created (derived) out of mass-motion into matter-time. It then becomes appropriate to consider whether mass has always existed. However, mass is a fifth-dimensional physical entity not accessible from empirical space-time references, except its presence in space-time is pervasive. The question is whether mass is an eternal entity or whether it was created out of a metaphysical process — a metaphysical energy transfer. In that case, the whole concept of Universal energy as a unity principle cannot be ignored.

Conclusion

The argument of an understanding of the Universe that theoretically evolved from a void must consider the present capability of human cognition (ego-consciousness) to comprehend/rationalize the concept of such a possibility.

We are attempting to look at Universal reality from the apparent known (five-dimensional model) to the unknown (void concept). Conceivably, rationalizing a "condition" that had no beginning. An implied "condition" associated with an energy transfer — leading to the consideration of Universal energy as a unity principle.

However, the theoretical requirements for the void concept are characterized by a "condition," and this condition is defined by the need for energy to sustain its "condition." Most importantly, from an a priori perspective, we have opened the door from a theoretical consideration of the Universal void concept to a hypothetical proposition based on the known empirical data base from our space-time continuum. We cannot simply dismiss the void as a possible "condition" of reality since physical reality arguably had a beginning. Again, if we accept the concept of a void being a "condition" of reality requiring energy to sustain its presence, then the energy to sustain the void must be provided from a unity energy principle.

Further, if the theoretical void concept that requires a "condition" is proved invalid, then from an a priori perspective, the Creator and the Universe are eternal. Appropriately, should the theoretical "condition" be proved valid, then the void concept (in an absolute sense) is invalid. It is an apparent conundrum except that the input considerations that support the valid/invalid conclusions of the "condition" are not quite the same, and the validity issue needs further discussion.

A void, without a "condition" entity, cannot exist in any concept of cognitive reality. It is absurd, certainly in an empirical scientific sense, for a void to self-generate into what we perceive as a space-time continuum. The reality of space-time (the physical product of that reality) did not proceed from an absolute void — it proceeded from a creation concept with all its attendant unified energy, motion, and cognition (its natural laws). This creationist concept and the Creator, by definition, are universal, immutable, and eternal. Moreover, the models suggest that these natural laws are not derived from our ego-conscious state of cognition, but rather from the Creator's own concept (a higher consciousness) of the infinite and the eternal. Through the Creator's nature, the evolutionary struggle for Universal understanding becomes the human task.

Correspondence on the Void Concept with Larry Staples, Ph.D., Jungian Analyst

Ken,

I admire and am impressed with your elegantly conceived and written paper, "The Void Concept," which is the latest in a growing collection of deep and interesting pieces. At the same time, I remain mindful that it is likely that I miss some of the meaning because of a huge deficiency on my part in scientific knowledge. For this reason, my understanding of your material of necessity has to fall back on intuition. Your education and work in engineering and physics have much better prepared you for this kind of exploration.

If I understand what you are arguing, your concept does help clarify for me the role and position of the void in creation. I believe you argue that the void logically cannot be entirely void, that you cannot create something out of nothing. Again, as I understand it, you point to the necessity of there being at least a metaphysical content to the void and that this content has to come from somewhere else, namely the fifth dimension. I think, if I am understanding properly, that you conclude the Void had to be created and sustained by the Creator who is found in, or actually is, the fifth dimension.

Larry

Larry,

I approached the void concept from a modified dialectic (Hegelian) approach, whereby a thesis (eternal Creator) is transformed into its opposite, an antithesis (void). Exploring the essence/contradictions of these concepts, my attempt was to reach a synthesis from these polarized positions and perhaps a higher level of understanding. The outcome of the proposition, for me, is that by definition the Creator is an eternal concept. This view is based on my hypothesis that any reality (including a void) must constitute a "condition" and that any "condition" requires energy (physical and/or metaphysical) to sustain it. The "condition" hypothesis obviates the concept of a void because energy in some form must be present to sustain it.

From your question, my abstract proposition leads me to conclude that the Creator is eternal if you accept the hypothesis that any reality constitutes a "condition" and any "condition" requires energy to sustain it. My hypothesis concludes that a universal void is an impossible concept and therefore that the Creator is eternal. The difficulty with these concepts — particularly the word eternal — is that we think in terms of time. Time is an implicit derivative of motion. It is a dimensional entity of our space-time continuum, and by its nature is finite. Motion is infinite (eternal). Time will cease when matter ceases.

Kenneth

Thoughts

Nature is alive. Nature is poetry — poetry in motion
Relentlessly in motion beyond all measures of time as we
　　sense it
This nature, exported from a creative place our living
　　hearts may never know
Perhaps only glimpsed through a shadowy urge and
　　perception
From the essence of the Creator's cognitive gift to
　　humankind.
Then, nature, alive and in motion,
Belongs to an inexorable, pervasive relationship with the
　　whole of reality.

BOOK TWO

Overview of Book Two

If you were to consider the question of the origin of our created empirical world (Big Bang Theory), you would be confronted with the overwhelming prospect of a creation system already operational in the Universe. Consider the "before" concept and the "after" concept. We are reasonably knowledgeable about the after concept (our empirical system), but the before concept and the critical creation event lead us to profoundly complex analyses.

What does it mean to say "before our created world began"? What conceptually does this condition suggest? It might suggest nothingness (a vacuum), a point source, or a limitless ether. Why would any of these conditions necessarily suggest that the concept "before our created world began" is valid? In this case, it may also be a manifestation of an unconscious cognitive imaging projection.

However, the other side of the "before the created world began" is that something was already operational in the Universe, whether it was energy or forces in nature, or both. This apparent condition leads us into a quandary. Logically, if something already existed, then the Universe was already in an operational process and capable of creation. It is reasonable to suggest that this "something" is of an eternal nature.

Given the rationale that there was something operational before our created world, we are confronted with the reality of the concept of a Creator. However, this revelation transcends the simple describing the behavior of our created world in terms of empirical functions and their evolutionary progression. However, the gift of cognition interferes with this limited perspective and introduces the idea of something inherently greater than the ego consciousness of humankind.

Now that we have introduced the concept of physical and metaphysical components of a complex universal reality, the issue becomes more complicated. On the one hand, we are quite aware of our created empirical system (space-time), but that fact requires the need to explore the system that produced our temporal world. Hypothetically, that system is introduced here as an eternal concept. This creation event underscores the act of giving life and cognition to an empirical human world. These gifts from the Creator imply an act from the Creator to extend an eternal system to a purposeful entropic world for some evolutionary purpose.

This creation event necessitates both new physical and metaphysical models of reality to a quantum reality. Book Two hypothesizes a model of the Creator to begin an understanding of our relationship to both the physical and the metaphysical aspects of reality.

The physical model (Book One) and the metaphysical model (Book Two) form an inseparable unity. They describe a functionally operational system where mass-motion provides the energy, along with the natural laws that provide the governing operation for the whole of reality.

The Creator

Introduction

A hypothesis relative to the Creator might reasonably begin with references to our collective Gods and to the study of theology. Theological approaches to the history of religious beliefs offer a path to consider our Gods in terms of the Creator, and the essence of the Creator in terms of our limited understanding of physical reality. It is imperative to understand the Creator in terms of theology and the Gods that have formed the whole of our collective religious experience.

The study of theology includes the concept of negative (apophatic) theology that attempts to describe God by negation – by what cannot be said about God. This apophatic concept accepts that God is ineffable, an abstract experience only recognized. Humans cannot describe the essence of God. However, Christianity and Judaism base their belief systems on revelation. In the case of Christianity, God inspired the writings of scripture revealing himself to humankind and incarnate in the person of Christ. In contrast to apophatic theology, Christian ideas about revelation present us with the prospect of philosophizing on a positive (cataphatic) theology that would include a hypothesis of the concept of a creator.

There is an urgency, a propensity, in the whole of the human spirit that seeks enlightenment beyond our apparent capacity to know the unknowable – sometimes without realizing that our limited perception of reality prevents us from a closer perspective of the Creator.

The Gods we experience are those God images that are provided to us in direct relationship to our particular genetic makeup, our tribal attitudes and customs, and our intellectual propensities. Progressive, historical-driven yearnings cultivate the social need for a particular God image.

God images are a gift from the Creator. They are a part of the Creator's plan to project an indirect experience of the Creator to humankind. This projection of Gods from the Creator (hypothesized as a fifth-dimensional concept) comes across a dimensional barrier to our space-time sense of reality. There is a common philosophical, psychological, and religious connection among all Gods. The basic differences between Gods could be considered as a ritualistic process – a process of respective tribal attitudes and tendencies.

The Creator Concept

The Creator of the Universe as a physical/metaphysical concept will be considered here from the perspective of my paper A Five-Dimensional Model of the Universe (Copyright, May 17, 2007, TXu1-358-083).

The nature of the physical Universe and the natural laws inherent in all things are the fundamental concepts that comprise the whole of our reality. They are the essence of the Creator's plan for our existence and purpose. An understanding of nature and its energies/processes is to define the Creator's plan and potentially to glimpse the purpose of an orderly, rational Universe. Study nature and the laws of nature, and you study the Creator. Understanding the creative process and the concept of universal reality with its complex, inextricably linked dimensional functions is to begin an understanding of nature and the nature of the Creator.

The basic philosophical notion of the Creator is the natural consequence of our being. The Creator concept! In that sense, and in a scientific sense, nature is our creator. Nature is our experience, our reality, our destiny.

Unfortunately, our scientific understanding of the physical nature of the Universe is compromised and limited by a continued adherence to a four-dimensional (space-time continuum) concept of universal reality. We conceptually experience, in our space-time reality, only those limited natural effects of the Creator's plan in its evolutionary and perceived chaotic processes.

My five-dimensional model of the Universe describes a mass/motion – space/time continuum. The fifth dimension is postulated as that region beginning at the interface of the sub-atomic particle domain (at the interface barrier). The fifth dimension is characterized as that region containing all the mass in our functional universal five-dimensional system. The fifth dimension is a displacement phenomenon from our four-dimensional space-time continuum. These corresponding dimensional realities are inter-related and provide the connected pathways for the creation, functioning, and understanding of the Universe.

The Creator in our space-time continuum sense of reality is a numinous concept: a concept incapable of being described or understood except as an experience or as a projection. Our pervading space-time concept of reality is a woefully limited and constrained box that requires us to imagine a Creator concept without a more complete perspective of universal reality. My five-dimensional concept of physical reality implies that our experience of the Creator image is engendered by a projection from a complex entity residing in the fifth dimension. In this context, the Creator concept is opened to the possibility of a hypothesis that attempts to describe or understand its nature.

The Creator must be explainable in terms of a complex physical reality that hypothesizes universal creation in relation to the source of its instigation and propagation. The origin of the Universe is not explainable in terms of a space-time continuum model of reality.

To conclude that the Creator is unknowable is a reflection of our present understanding of universal reality. Our physical reality (space-time continuum) provides only an outward physical image of the Universe. Its limitations focus our perceptions of the Creator only through individual mystical experiences.

The purpose of this paper is to consider a perception of the Creator based on a relativistically internalized fifth-dimensional concept.

This five-dimensional model, along with the natural effects of our space-time continuum concept of reality, leads toward the hypothesis that the fifth dimension mass-motion content is the physical source energy instigator of the Universe. In conjunction with the physical energy component (mass-motion) is the crucial metaphysical component that defines the Creator's intellectual process. Within this complex fifth-dimensional structure, the Creator is the seed of all existence, of all mass-motion and matter-time. The Creator is the whole of that which creates and powers the Universe.

The Creator

My hypothesis is that the Creator is a fifth-dimensional concept. The Creator is a single-unit entity that incorporates two fundamental components: A mass-motion component that provides the physical energy to create and sustain our Universe; and a metaphysical (reconciled tension) component that is the intellectual essence that activates the Creator's plan for the Universe and provides the metaphysical energy that governs the natural laws of the Universe.

The Creator is not an invention of consciousness but rather is pre-existent to consciousness. However, from conscious observation, the Creator has instilled instinctual images within the framework of psychic consciousness so that humans can experience the Creator.

In Jungian theory, these instinctual images are called archetypes. Archetypes pre-exist consciousness and condition conscious processes. Archetypes are attributes of instincts (a part of the particular nature of perceptions) and only the collective component of a perception. These images of the psyche are eternal, repeatable, and universal. These archetypal images and motifs pervade our conscious and unconscious psyches and dwell in the deep recesses of a collective unconscious region.

From an archetypal or motif perspective, the Creator can be perceived as a mandala. Jung's concept of the mandala is a circle, a symbol of wholeness that contains all the energies and patterns in a visualized realm of the Creator. Jung says: "The mandala symbolizes, by its central point, the ultimate unity off all archetypes as well as the multiplicity of the phenomenal world, and is therefore the empirical equivalent of the metaphysical concept of a unus mundus" (Collected Works, Vol. 14, paragraph 661).

The two fundamental components of the Creator within this mandala are hypothesized as:

- The mass-motion component of the fifth dimension that provides the physical energy to create and perpetuate the Universe.
- The metaphysical component of the fifth dimension comprises the Creator's immutable natural laws, the reconciliation of the opposites, a higher level of consciousness (beyond ego-consciousness), and the essence of being.

A visual interpretation of the Creator as a mandala is omnipresent in the whole of physical energy in conjunction with metaphysical contents. The inter-connecting links and interactive pathways between these two components are integrated and reconciled by their respective operational functions.

Physical Energy Component

The physical aspects of the Creator are omnipresent in the core of the fifth dimension, functioning as the energy engine of the Universe in the form of mass-motion entities. (See my paper, "A Fifth-Dimensional Model of the Universe.")

Metaphysical Component

The great abundance of physical evidence supporting the idea of universal natural laws leads me to postulate that any universal event/action cannot occur from physical forces alone. It is insufficient for events/actions to occur without a metaphysical component. Every event/action has its purpose, its consequences, and its complex myriad of interrelated effects and counter-effects. Every event/action is defined by a complex plan that is governed by universal laws. The natural laws of the Universe are a metaphysical concept. The Universe is a specifically defined and thoughtful plan of the Creator.

The Creator is hypothesized as omnipresent in a mandala unifying the mass-motion component of physical energy with its component of metaphysical entities. The Creator is an all-pervading energy mandala in a totally efficient benign stasis of perfect symmetry where these components are fully integrated, reconciled, and all-powerful.

Comments on The Creator

- The Creator resides in the fifth dimension. There is no direct dimensional relationship between the Creator and our created space-time continuum sense of physical reality (matter).
- The critical cognitive influence on the creation of our space-time continuum is the function of the metaphysical component of the Creator's whole. The natural laws of the Universe provide the mechanism that activates the process of creation and the process of localized re-generation.
- This paper hypothesizes a Creator model in relation to a single eternal entity comprising both physical and metaphysical concepts. These specific concepts will be expanded to explain further the physical functions of the Creator, along with another paper focused on the complex nature of the metaphysical concepts operational in the Creator's whole. The natural laws, consciousness, and essence of being, along with the reconciliation of the opposites, are metaphysical concepts in need of further elucidation.

Correspondence on The Creator with Larry Partain, Ph.D. Physicist

Ken,

I enjoyed reading your Creator manuscript that is a follow-up to the fifth-dimensional manuscript. I certainly feel there is a spiritual dimension to the human experience that goes beyond the four dimensions of time and space. And I have no trouble referring to it as a fifth dimension. In fact, I rather like it. I certainly feel more comfortable with it than with the 10 or 11 dimensional space of the current string theory proposed by some theoretical physicists. However, there are important differences. Quantum mechanics comes up with mathematical equation descriptions of nature that can be and have been experimentally tested and found to be extremely accurate in predicting outcomes and controlling results. The latter includes solar energy conversion that is daily producing gigawatts of electric power from sunlight in reliable ways that may well provide the best electric energy source of the future worldwide. That is, the outcomes arise from scientifically applying quantum mechanical principles to provide important outcomes that are undoubtedly real even if their microscopic basis appears far from any common sense reality. It is such experimental tests that make quantum mechanics science something hard to believe, even if it could be actual reality.

Your fifth-dimensional hypothesis is also different from string theory in that it does not predict any new experimental phenomena tests with some unique predicted and testable results. However, yours shares a property with string theory that neither one has something that can be construed measurable in terms of current technology.

String theory predicts experimental results, but ones that require accelerator energy levels many orders of magnitude above any machines that can even be projected to exist for decades or maybe even centuries. Hence, neither your theory nor string theory can be currently put to any experimental scientific test. Both should be considered philosophy until they can. Describing your hypothesis and string theory as philosophy is not a criticism. Philosophy occupies a very important and critical position in the history of thought and the progression of human history. In my mind, science deals with only the small portion of human experience that is reproducible, predictable, and controllable. Most of my experiences and life pathways have felt unique and largely not well controlled and hence not scientific. It is these un-controlled elements of the major part of my life that I need to have some spiritual ways of comprehending and dealing with my existence. Spirituality has apparently been a strong need sought universally throughout history. The bottom line is that I was stimulated by your latest writing and enjoyed reading it and considering its arguments and concepts that feel much more comfortable to me than those proposed by many current day theoretical physicists.

Larry

Larry,

I read with great interest the draft of a section of the book you are editing. You have looked into the world of quantum mechanics since Planck's groundbreaking explanation of black body radiation in 1900 and have observed the mysteries of a reality beyond classical physics. Quantum mechanics (the study of motion, quanta, and probabilities) is the window through which the fifth dimension is indirectly observed. The observations from DeBroglie, Compton, Scrodinger, and others are fifth-dimensional effects relative to the experiment under test. The wave-particle duality is an example of the predictable complex behavior of mass-motion. Also, note the 1955 Nobel Laureate Willis Lamb's work, "The Lamb Shift," which is a tiny deviation in the energy of an electron orbiting a hydrogen atom nucleus. My interpretation is that this energy shift is a fifth-dimensional effect on Bohr's model of the atom.

Thank you for your penetrating comments on The Creator. Your argument for experimentally tested and repeated, accurate scientific results is unequivocally valid. The valid of quantum mechanics to accurately predict the probability of quanta in motion is unassailable. Quantum mechanics and all of quantum physics provide the only proven mathematical discipline available to understand our Universe and its reality. My hypothesis of the fifth dimension rests on the validity of quantum physics. The hypothesis has no value — either physically or philosophically — without the foundation of quantum physics.

The critical issue is that quantum mechanics cannot be directly interpreted into a Newtonian concept of reality. The only model that science understands (Einstein could not get past this concept) is a space-time continuum box. That space-time box was plowed under by Planck's experiment in 1900 and followed up with repeatable observations by dozens of other experimenters since that time. We need a new model of reality. We don't understand the relationship between mass and matter, as if they were the same or primarily the same concept in the same dimensional construct.

I was touched by your comments on my paper. We share some of the same views and uncertainties regarding metaphysical concepts. Spirituality is a universal human experience, and it flows from the Creator's metaphysical component. Unfortunately, metaphysical experiences are not reproducible, predictable, or controllable in our space-time continuum world. However, this metaphysical component with the mandala whole of the Creator is the repository of all the natural laws of the Universe. These natural laws are unassailable and are as constant as the physical reality the Creator produced. This spiritual and philosophical issue is at the root of my next paper, "The Why of the Creator."

Kenneth

Ken,

It does look like the number of dimensions that physicists consider is going up. Now if only someone could make some sense of this without going to a ridiculous number of dimensions! Did the Higgs evolve out of the big bang or somewhere/sometime else? Interesting puzzles.

Larry

Larry,

I have been reading the recent reports on the identification of a Higgs boson-like particle. They have apparently been able to identify traces or effects of a massive elementary particle to resolve inconsistencies in the Standard Model of particle physics.

It is interesting that the Higgs boson is referred to as the "God particle" since it purports to explain how elementary particles obtain their mass. A better reference would be the "Creator particle" since we are dealing here with fifth-dimensional physical and metaphysical effects. We are beginning to look into the "window" of the fifth dimension as we press our dim lights across the interface of a more complete understanding of universal reality.

The most amazing thing to me is that the scientific community is being led to the threshold of accepting universal reality as something beyond our space-time continuum. A place beyond the physical that can be understood in mathematical terms — the eternal calculus.

My models (Fifth Dimension, Creator) hypothesize that the Higgs boson is a fifth-dimensional particle as are all subatomic particles. In that sense, the Higgs boson preceded the "beginning" of our space-time continuum. (I leave the discussion of the "big bang" to a more in-depth future discussion.) My models support the contention that the Creator is eternal (beyond time) and that the whole of reality is constituted from the physical and metaphysical components of the Creator residing in the fifth dimension.

Kenneth

Correspondence on The Creator with Larry Staples, Ph.D., Jungian Analyst

Ken,

I enjoyed our visit and our conversation. I have the sense that you have found a calling in your new concepts and models, and that your opus continues to unfold. Once the seed is planted, we never know what the end may be. I can see you are brimming with still more ideas that you intend to express as time marches on.

As I thought about your notions of the reconciliation of the opposites, we may not be as far apart as I first thought. If by reconciliation you mean they can exist side by side despite their tension, then I agree. If you envision a union of opposites, then it's hard for me to imagine that condition in a conscious state. It certainly may exist in some unconscious state, as we simply don't know what happens in that state. If your writing goes like mine, it tends to evolve over time as new insights keep appearing. That's what makes the experience so rich. I feel like you are on a journey that is of great importance to you and, hopefully, to others.

Larry

Larry,

Thank you for your comments on my paper, The Creator. Your observation on the metaphysical component of my Creator model as fundamentally a fifth-dimensional concept is exactly correct. In a fully reconciled, differentiated state, the opposites would have no tension and therefore no consciousness. That condition is a key component of the model. A question that I hope to answer in my third paper is: What is the Creator's relationship not only to the fifth dimension but also to the whole of reality (all five dimensions) and whether — in a metaphysical sense — men (or any carrier of intelligence) can become one with the Creator through a final evolutionary process that reconciles and integrates the complexity and energy of the opposites.

Kenneth

Correspondence on The Creator with Norman Theiss, Lutheran Pastor

Kenneth,

You describe relativity as part of the essence of the Creator. Is there no existence outside this relativity and is our existence dependent on a relationship to a thinking mind (the Creator) as well as the thinking minds of the created? Is our consciousness limited to the Creator's higher consciousness?

Norm

Norm,

Relativity comes to us as a first principle of nature. It is the essence of nature and its laws and, by extension, is part of the Creator's metaphysical self.

I am having difficulty understanding your comment of "no existence outside this relativity" The structure of the whole Universe is comprised of a physical component in conjunction with its related metaphysical natural laws in a complex system of reality. My models will not allow an existence outside this sense of reality. Also, I would refer to the Creator in terms of an evolved cognitive presence rather than a "thinking mind." The thinking mind is what we homo sapiens have to offer as a part of the Creator's plan for our creation. Relativity permeates the whole of existence.

My models would not accept the concept of an "existence" beyond the Creator's whole — the concept would have no meaning other than ego speculation.

Yes, I believe that our consciousness (ego) is derived from the Creator's higher consciousness — by design. I also believe that this derivation is a critical part of the Creator's plan for us to evolve. But "linked" is an interesting concept. Can we aspire to reach a level of consciousness assumed by the Creator? Not in our empirical world, because we have no direct knowledge of the Creator's realm. We have a hypothesis. Fortunately, we have what might be considered as "patterns" of logical behavior in nature. The immutable natural laws that govern the Universe provide our guide to an understanding of the logic inherent in the operation of the Universe.

Kenneth

The Metaphysical Nature of the Creator

My model of the Creator (see my paper "The Creator) hypothesizes a single unity entity comprising two fundamental components:

- A physical entity (mass-motion) that provides the energy engine for the whole Universe.
- A metaphysical entity that provides for the operation and governance of the whole Universe through an interconnected system of natural laws.

My earlier papers have expanded on the physical characteristics of the Creator model related to a five-dimensional model of the Universe. This paper expands the metaphysical aspects of the Creator in relation to a higher level of consciousness that is characterized by natural laws that operate the whole Universe.

The Creator is the seed of all being. The whole of that seed includes all cognitive contents (conscious/unconscious) that represent the essence of metaphysical reality.

The metaphysical component of the Creator's "whole" is made up primarily of the nature of things, along with the reconciliation of the opposites, a higher level of consciousness (beyond ego consciousness) and a divine essence of being. The metaphysical whole of the Creator is an eternal concept (beyond entropic considerations), residing in the fifth dimension.

The Natural Laws

Our relationship to the Creator may be understood in terms of the nature of things. Universal natural laws are a fundamental aspect of the Creator's metaphysical whole. These natural laws are complex and varied and include:

- The calculus: the mathematics of change, of shifting quantities and dimensions.
- The laws of thermodynamics. The behavior of physical entities are governed and modified by these laws. They are applicable to our space-time continuum in a matter-time mode, but they also operate in a mass-motion mode outside the boundaries of entropic systems. The operation of any Universal system is controlled by the natural law or laws prescribing its particular Universal function.
- The laws of gravity. These laws are correlated in space-time to provide the mechanism for the operation and function of our galaxies and solar systems. In a broader perspective, the laws of gravity operate in a corresponding fifth-dimensional mode (mass-motion) to provide for the functional operation of the whole of the physical Universe.

In a five-dimensional Universal sense, the natural laws of the Creator are characterized by a unified principle operating to balance the whole of the Universe for the purpose of its efficient operation and function.

The Reconciliation of the Opposites

The ego-conscious psychology of humankind contains a broad spectrum or patterns of concepts/ideas that have been described as the opposites. The whole spectrum of cognition is rife with opposites (light/dark, good/evil, strong/weak, etc.). In an ego-conscious attitude, our response to these opposites has been to rationalize a conditional, polarized perspective. As an example, using good and evil as a particular polarized attitude, the rationale has been an attempt to expiate evil as a worthy goal to our collective reasoning. However, good/evil is a spectrum/tapestry of a metaphysical reality that pre-exists ego consciousness and is eternal in concept. Good and evil reside in the Creator's metaphysical realm at a higher level of consciousness (beyond ego) where the respective opposites are reconciled and integrated as a united whole. The total effect of the spectrum/tapestry of any pair of opposites in the fifth dimensional realm is beneficial, not malignant.

As stated above, the metaphysical opposites are pre-existent to consciousness. The opposites are eternal and are patterns of the Creator's work and intent. They are innate, primal, archetypal images or patterns from the instinctual fifth dimension realm and are part of the Creator's metaphysical whole. They are an eternal concept and are part of the instinctual condition that represents the laws of the Universe. They are behavioral patterns that formulate the intellectual (philosophical) content in our conscious/unconscious existence. They represent the metaphysical energy latent in the interrelated complexity (tension) of the whole of the opposites' spectrum (pattern).

A discussion of the opposites will necessarily lead to the coniunctio, defined as the uniting of separate qualities or an equalization of principles. The factors that come together are conceived as opposites in confrontation with or attraction to one another. They form a complex pattern (good/evil, love/hate, active/passive, etc.) of these factors.

The difficulty in hypothesizing the opposites as the essence of metaphysical energy is that certain opposites are characterized as physical entities, while others are metaphysically structured. A pair of opposites may contain, by definition or reasoning, both physical and metaphysical contents. For example, it would seem apparent that lightness and darkness are fundamentally physical opposites, while good and evil represent metaphysical attitudes. In another case, the opposites of masculine and feminine seem to embody characteristics both physical and metaphysical.

We cannot divorce ourselves from the qualitative unity factors of the opposites because they represent those opposites that are inherent in the physical component of the Creator's presence. They are intrinsically linked to the Creator's physical plan for our five-dimensional reality. However, we must be primarily attentive to those opposites that are the essence of metaphysical energy. They are the opposites that concern themselves primarily with the equalization of metaphysical principles.

The hypothesis of the opposites as the metaphysical component of the Creator must consider that all the opposites are included and present in the Creator's whole presence (the mandala or seed). By definition, the two fundamental components of the Creator require a connective, interactive link from physical to metaphysical functions. Also, the opposites are pre-existent to consciousness and represent patterns of the Creator's work.

The relationship between all the opposites, their inherent physical characteristics or metaphysical attitudes, form a connective whole of the Creator's functional operations. In this sense, the opposites provide the crucial connected pathways that link and coordinate the physical and metaphysical aspects of their reconciled nature.

The opposites are collectively referred to as all those aspects of metaphysical cognizance and perception that define a complex intra/inter relationship to our universal reality. The relationship between good/evil, love/hate, active/passive, etc. are examples of the metaphysical energy manifest in the opposites. In a visual context, the opposites could be considered as a polar concept (in dramatic tension) or as a complex tapestry (a directly interconnected pattern of functional efficiency). Their respective metaphysical energy is inefficiently minimized at their poles (undifferentiated) and maximized at the center (differentiated). In a polarized state, they are unfocused, diffused, and unreconciled to their complementary opposites. They operate in a dysfunctional mode, with an inefficient use of directed energy. In contradistinction, opposites reconciled and integrated as a unity (a complete spectrum) would operate in a totally efficient state. The energy of the unity of the opposites would not only be totally efficient but essentially unassailable. The fifth-dimensional concept that the opposites are fully reconciled argues that the stasis inherent in that condition is the core of its fundamental energy.

The hypothesis of the opposites as a source of the metaphysical component of the Creator requires that the respective conflicting forces in each opposite must be integrated and reconciled — not overcome. The concept that good and evil, for example, can be overcome (eliminated) would theoretically reduce its metaphysical energy to a non-functional condition.

The idea that the opposites, good and evil, could be overcome does not consider that these concepts are metaphysical and pre-existent to consciousness. They are eternal concepts. In an differentiated mode (fifth dimension), there is no tension or conflict that compromises or distorts the energy that is manifest in the unity of the opposites. However, in the undifferentiated mode (space-time continuum), the opposites are polarized, in conflict (tension), and are disruptive. In either mode, their total energy levels are intrinsically the same.

The opposites as a complete entity, good or evil, are malleable concepts in our space-time continuum. They are the clay of the Creator's work for us. They are philosophical concepts/ideas that would be devoid of any meaningful content, of any focused energy, without reference or consideration to their interactive opposites.

The opposites that are projected upon us in a polarized state are a fundamental and critical aspect of the Creator's purpose in the plan for our universal destiny. The reconciliation of the opposites is the essential condition, the *sine qua non*, that elevates metaphysical energy to its full and total completeness. The reconciliation of the opposites is a fundamental truth of our whole Universe and of the natural laws that govern us.

A Higher Level of Consciousness

My model of the Creator outlines two primary levels of consciousness:

- The Creator's fifth dimension consciousness that is universally operational and functional within its metaphysical core structure. It is a consciousness beyond ego.
- An ego-consciousness that resulted from the differentiated creation of our space-time continuum through the advent of the Creator's implicit intent and action. (See my paper, "A Fifth Dimensional Model of the Universe.")

By definition, these two levels of consciousness are related, but they have been differentiated (diffused) through the creation process from a higher level of consciousness into our ego-conscious space-time level. As stated, the Creator's consciousness is without ego. Its function is systematic. Its objective is focused toward a benign state of perfection. In this attitude, its higher level of consciousness operates and directs the Creator's natural laws toward the operation and function of all Universal systems.

A higher level of consciousness is implicit in the operational function of the Universe. It is the perfect level of consciousness without ego-drive motives or considerations. It contains an attitude of acceptance, particularly the acceptance of the full range of the spectrum of the opposites.

The process toward a higher level of consciousness is a process of integration. In the calculus of natural laws, the integration process is inclusionary and accepting — but even more it embraces every element of metaphysical reality. In contrast, the calculus process of differentiation provides a diffusion function that scatters the core of complete unity into patterns of polarized contents. Personal, self-driven contents.

A cognitive, evolutionary process beyond the ego-conscious attitude will be an extraordinary journey into understanding. The struggle will be to evolve beyond an acceptance of a diffused, polarized spectrum of opposites toward the reconciliation of those opposites through a process of cognitive integration. The integration of the opposites is unresolvable with an ego-driven attitude. This journey toward philosophical and religious understanding must leave behind the primitive and instinctual process that were a vital part of our nascent survival attitude. The benefits of this empirical sense of reality have been abundant and extraordinarily useful. They encompass the material treasures we know today. They explain our societal priorities, but they encompass only an aspect of our reality. The Creator and the creation process is the whole of Universal reality.

The Divine Essence of Being

The Creator is the divine essence of being. An entity that permeates the nature of all Universal constructs, both physical and metaphysical. An eternal entity, functioning in the whole of the Universe that has provided a plan for the continuous operation of the whole, natural Universal system.

Before we proceed, it is necessary to understand that we are here considering two respective hypotheses. First, we have our empirical model of reality called our four-dimensional space-time continuum. Beyond empiricism, there is another model of reality hypothesized as a five-dimensional model of the Universe. In essence,

- Our empirical model of reality was created. Space-time is an entropic system and it is a temporal entity.
- The fifth-dimensional model — including our created space-time model — is both entropic and eternal. The fifth dimension itself is an eternal entity and provides

the physical and metaphysical operating system for the whole of the Universe. The fifth dimension is the domain of the Creator.

The divine being of the Creator is manifested in a complex Universal system of eternal, related natural laws. These natural laws operate to provide the operation and function of both our empirical space-time system and my five-dimensional model of reality.

Our space-time continuum was created by the Creator. In this creation process, the Creator theoretically had a purpose and a plan for this act of creation. From this supposition, it logically follows that the act of creation includes an essence (a fundamentally differentiated aspect) of the Creator's whole into the creation of our space-time continuum. In effect and by extension, the Creator's presence is latent in our space-time creation process. From this analysis, it follows that an essence of the Creator is latent in every cell, both organic and inorganic, within our created system. In conjunction with this act of creation was the advent of the gift of cognition ordained by the Creator to humankind. Extending this concept is the connecting principle that the Creator had a purpose for the creation process. In that cognitive sense, the Creator has called the created to seek a path of evolutionary development toward a higher level of consciousness.

It would be a long and arduous journey to an attitude beyond ego-consciousness and toward a greater understanding of the Creator and the creative process. The argument is made that the cognitive processes that we possess (ordained by creation) are in some diffused manner related to the Creator's whole. There seems to be a rational choice to be made between a benign acceptance of our relationship to the

Creator based on the unknowable or a cognitive attempt to reach a higher level of consciousness on a dark, diffused path.

Is it a rational goal for the created soul to understand more of the Creator, or are we forever bound to muddle through our existence yoked to the wheel of empirical reality? It is a reasonable, cognitive probability that the Creator had a purpose for this act of creation along with the fact that this act of creation was latent with the gift of cognition. This act of creation defines the beginning of Universal discovery and provides the key not only to the whole of physical reality but to the understanding of all reality — physical and metaphysical.

The other side of this perspective is to argue that the root of Universal reality (the Creator) is unknowable and to assume that the creation of the Universe was a random event without benefit of conscious actions. The fundamental thread of this attitude may be rooted in an apparent lack of trust in Universal natural laws and, by extension, may contain a sense of loss of self worth attributed to an attitude focused on the ego-self.

For humankind, the cognitive recognition of the essence of the Creator and the creation process is inescapable. Our collective journey to this understanding may take a thousand generations or more, but all paths must lead to the purpose of creation and to the essence of the Creator. The fundamental question is whether we are up to the task of exploring higher levels of consciousness.

The Creator's Realm

Introduction

An unfortunate consequence resulting from the history of western scientific inquiry is the limited idea that our empirical world is simply a random event, a chaotic circumstance without a cognitive plan or sense of purpose. This unfortunate consequence results in a hopeless cynicism perceived as reality. A root of this perspective may be fostered by the notion that empirical science is circumscribed simply by the physical world with its fundamental doctrinaire requirement for repeatable, experimental results. Somehow this belief seems to persist in the face of proven metaphysical laws of nature, either misunderstood or ignored. This hidebound attitude is masking the prospect of exploring a quantum perspective of reality in conjunction with our ongoing exploration of the empirical world. Our age-old scientific models and attitudes are frustrating the attempts to meld all of those new, complex, extraordinary wonders for us to contemplate and understand.

My hypothetical model of the Creator (see my paper "The Creator") in conjunction with my Five-Dimensional Model of the Universe characterizes the Creator realm as a fifth-dimensional entity of an eternal nature. This realm is configured from a physical (mass-motion) component in conjunction with its metaphysical (the natural laws) component. The Creator is a singular entity comprising these two fundamental components. The Creator resides in the fifth dimension as an eternal concept and as the creative force whose cognitive initiative created our entropic space-time continuum world.

The Creator resides in a dimension beyond space and time and is the actuator of the whole of universal reality, including our empirical (space-time) world. My models contend that the creation of space-time was not a random event nor was the advent of that creation process in any sense chaotic (uncontrolled). Our space-time continuum is simply an entropic, ecological system, spectacular in its developmental process, but not chaotic.

Universal natural laws govern the order and the process of entropic systems as well as eternal systems. The metaphysical laws of nature are unassailable in all universal systems. There are no deviations in natural law functions particularly related to created systems (entropic). Functionally, there may be differences in particular operational activities between dimensionally separated entropic and eternal systems.

Our created space-time system is also imperfect in the manner and sense of its cognitive, conscious attitude. It is an ego-conscious attitude that particularly seems to attempt eradication rather than reconciliation of the opposites in our nature. The opposites form a metaphysical spectrum of universal norm (a complex patten of reality) which is fundamentally related to a process of integration (rather than differentiation) focused toward reconciliation of any opposite condition (i.e., good vs. evil).

The Fifth Dimensional Realm

Is there something out there? Technological developments are leading us to the complex world of the sub-atomic realm to regions that were only speculative before the 20th century. This new technology is allowing us a glimpse of these curious observations that are being interpreted as anomalies or irregularities in the common (empirical) order of things. The principle of uncertainty and the idea of superposition (quantum indeterminacy) are examples of anomalies that are now viewed as observers' paradoxes seen through the lens of a four-dimensional model of reality.

These extraordinary technological developments are leading us to a new realm of universal reality — to a quantum perspective that seeks an expanding model of reality and suggests the idea of a new dimensional concept. A new model that accepts the hypothesis of an entropic system (space-time) operating in conjunction with, and functionally operated by, a non-entropic (eternal) system — in this case the fifth dimension. This paper attempts to explore the region of an eternal system that contains and operates the whole of reality — the Creator's realm.

Universal reality cannot be fully understood in terms of an empirical system, i.e., our classical space-time continuum. There are any number of scientific examples which would support the argument for this case. One does not have to look any further than the natural laws of thermodynamics to reach this conclusion. Simply stated, an entropic system is in a state of decay at inception. Such a system has a specific lifetime. By definition, an entropic system is incapable of creation, not of itself nor any issue. All entropic systems were created or regenerated by a system beyond entropy — a non-entropic eternal system.

My model would hypothesize that the fifth dimension realm is:

- Eternal
- Physical
- Metaphysical
- Cognitive
- Totally efficient
- The source of creation

This hypothetical realm is important toward understanding the concept of an eternal system and the need to explore its functions vis-a-vis our empirical sense of reality. As an example of this need is the idea of infinity.

Infinity is defined as the quality or condition of unbounded space, time, or quantity. Basically, this definition is an empirical idea derived from sense data or impressions. The empiricist philosopher John Locke believed that we can have no proper idea of the infinite. He argued that all sensory impressions are inherently finite, and so too are our thoughts and ideas.

The concept of infinity has puzzled and perplexed philosophers, including Locke, throughout the ages in their attempts to understand the idea, using empirical logic. Other attempts, including numbering systems, were employed to probe the length and breadth of infinite space without complete results.

Infinity is a concept beyond the empirical perspective. It is not a space-time continuum concept. Attempts to measure infinity are, by definition, finite. Infinity is a metaphysical concept and it belongs to the natural order of cosmology. It can be hypothesized and mathematically interpreted within the natural laws of mathematics (the calculus), but it is immeasurable in any empirical sense of reality. The concept of infinity exists outside empirical reality, but only in an eternal system. In an entropic system, infinity has no function, no operational purpose for its relational existence. Infinity can be intuited from a combination of physical and metaphysical entities, but its operational function is to define and regulate an eternal system in precise, constant motion.

The fifth dimension includes all available physical mass content along with the metaphysical natural laws that govern the functional operation of an eternal system in precise, constant motion. The natural laws imply the presence of a cognitive function operating as a level of consciousness beyond the ego structure. It is a realm that is integrated, resolved, and without conflict. It is a perfect operating system that embodies the full spectrum of all cognitive activity in a completely integrated and reconciled state of being. Universal activities flowing from this system carry out the intent and purpose of the Creator's plan.

The Eternal System

What is an eternal universal system?
- It is a non-entropic entity.
- It possesses all the mass energy in the whole Universe.
- Motion (the integral of time) is an absolute constant operating in a precise relationship for universal functions.
- It is a totally efficient operating system.
- Within the context of its physical and metaphysical structure, it knows no boundaries or operational limitations that might impede its eternal process.

- Its cognitive function operates at a fully individuated, higher level of consciousness beyond the ego attitude.

The eternal system's operating elements are mass-motion and the natural laws. The eternal system is connected to our entropic system (space-time) through an implicit differentiation process of change of state creation. This eternal system connection provides the essential link to the Creator's realm and to its plan for the creation of space-time. This conceptual idea is theoretically insinuating a complex cognitive process in two planes of reference that relate an integrated, reconciled level of consciousness to the struggle of ego-consciousness toward an evolutionary physical/metaphysical development cycle for its sentient species.

How does an eternal system operate? It operates through an efficient process of integrated, reconciled consciousness in conjunction with the auspices of natural laws. It contains all the latent physical (mass) energy available in the Universe for specific operational purposes.

The eternal nature of all things is in constant motion (an absolute universal constant). An eternal system cannot operate without motion and, by extension, cannot tolerate an "absolute solid" condition in any sense of universal reality. Despite our limited understanding and knowledge of the fundamental building blocks of the eternal system and their behavior (the physical sub-atomic realm), these basic particles remain separate entities under all natural, quiescent conditions. Otherwise, the effects would be cataclysmic.

The Creator's Essence

The Creator is hypothesized as a unity entity that comprises both physical and metaphysical components. The Creator resides in the fifth dimension as the whole of a complex eternal system. A question within the context of this fifth dimensional realm is: How can we contemplate understanding the aura of the Creator itself? Theoretically, it is reasonable to consider the Creator as a mandala image. Fundamentally, the image would be the seed from which all forms of creative energy flow. It would possess all the necessary prerequisite energy to operate functionally and maintain this eternal system including any and all created systems.

The seed is eternal and self-sustaining. The Creator is a unity, omnipotent, omnipresent, and cognitively aware of the nature of all things. The Creator is the guiding force and the light of all universal existence. Within this mandala resides a cognitive entity that can activate mass energy and its natural laws to operate and/or create/regenerate the whole Universe.

Is it possible to begin an understanding of the Creator's aura in relation to physical/metaphysical terms? In physical terms, we can hypothesize the mandala image as an ordinarily minute entity capable of extraordinary energy bursts. The physical energy bursts must be mass induced in a constant motion related activity. The physical presence of the Creator is united in the power of the unlimited energy available in the fifth dimension. This physical presence is characterized by a nature of complex universal functions and purposes that are the building blocks of all creative actions.

In metaphysical terms, we are dealing with cognition and the natural laws that govern the operation of the Universe. The Creator provides all the cognitive energy that emanates from the natural laws for the operation of the Universe. The natural laws are the foundation of pure cognitive expression. They extend their perception to all the tentacles of conscious and unconscious reason that unite the disciplines of the collective trinity (philosophy, psychology, and religion).

We are connected to the Creator as a consequence of the creation process. As a species, we contain the essence of the Creator's whole. We represent an element of a complex creation plan. This complex plan includes the Creator's gift of cognition to us that implies a sense of evolutionary development to reach for a higher level of consciousness beyond the nascent ego. A long period of trial and growth.

This evolutionary growth process is connected to the life cycle of our solar system. Our entropic planet Earth will theoretically continue for thousands of generations to prosper and discover the purpose of our existence. This ecologically efficient planet provides the necessary sustenance and the energy for this complex process to evolve. It also provides the metaphysical laws of nature inherent in the DNA/RNA codes for the species to functionally operate the ecological and social system required to collectively advance the evolutionary cycle.

Each generation has the opportunity to advance the cycle of evolutionary growth. The collective progression of data (positive or negative) is indelibly recorded on the modulated cycle of time for our continuing responsibility and potential posterity.

The myriad of human lives from each and every generation influence the cognitive progress of our collective history, adding to or subtracting from the purpose and intent of the Creator's plan. It is the sum of a written history of the human condition and forms the essence of a task to individually understand our connection to the Creator and the purpose of our creation.

Correspondence on the Creator's Realm with Peter Kearney, former Priest

Kenneth,

I was struck with your easy affirmation of the Creator as omnipotent. In the face of so many evils in our world, thinkers wonder whether the Creator can do all that has been attributed to that power. I have been seriously questioning the omnipotence of God myself, wondering whether the divinity is in process just as the world is in process. Carl Jung was open to such an idea, with God needing to justify himself by sending Jesus to us. He certainly lodged the original evil in the divinity and perhaps in a sense you do as well, though you insist these opposites are in complete reconciliation in the Creator.

Several questions occur to me as follows:

I notice how you often use the word "concept" as if it means "reality."

Were you opposing the philosophical idea that our knowledge is only of our own concepts that whether they correspond to a reality we can't really know? I like what you did, for I think the right view is that our knowledge is a knowledge of what is and not just merely of our own ideas.

That is quite a view, that theoretically there is no limit to our understanding of the whole Universe, including the Creator. Then, the Creator is not unknowable to us inasmuch as we are extensions of the Creator's whole. Might that mean we would eventually become omniscient ourselves?

You regard the purpose of our being here on earth in an evolutionary sense, in that we will eventually understand it all when it finally does happen.

Your thoughts proceed with reflections on rationality as a bond with the Creator. Is there room here for the Creator's love? Do we affirm divine love too readily in your view? Perhaps the Creator's decision to share with us through the act of cognition is love in itself.

Peter

Peter,

Thank you for your email.

My models insist that the opposites are in complete reconciliation in the Creator. The Creator possesses a higher level of consciousness (beyond ego). It is a fundamental principle in the eternal Creator's realm — beyond entropy and the empirical reality of the creation process.

I do not mean to imply that the idea of "concept" means "reality." I am suggesting that certain empirical ideas like entropy and matter do not exist in an eternal system. It is critically important to understand that the Creator's Whole (the metaphysical natural laws plus mass as the universal energy system) are eternal concepts residing in the fifth dimension. A key point is that the Creator resides in a dimension displaced from our empirical reality as a conceptual entity beyond my sensate powers to clearly articulate the form. However, my models are convinced that the Creator created our space-time continuum as a differentiated part of universal reality. Again, mass is an eternal physical energy entity operating in the fifth dimension, intimately related to, but differentiated from, what we call matter.

My models would argue that we cannot become omniscient ourselves. However, this idea is made exceedingly complex by the Creator's gift to us of cognizance in the creation process. This fact implies that we are endowed with an "essence" of the Creator's Whole. In that sense, we have the prospect of reaching a higher level of consciousness and cognitive integration. In Jungian terms, our personal struggle is keyed toward a process of individuation.

My models would not deny the prospect of a dimensional connection with the Creator, but not in a physical, entropic sense. Entry into the fifth-dimensional realm could potentially be a metaphysical process of integration (cognitive) and a higher level of consciousness.

The question of whether the act of creation is love in itself is thoughtful and quite beautiful. In any sense of reality, the spectrum of the opposites is omnipresent. The question is whether they are polarized or whether they are reconciled. In a functional sense, the opposites are integrated (reconciled) in the Creator's realm, and they are differentiated (polarized) in the creation (entropic) process. In other words, the Creator has embraced (reconciled) the spectrum of the opposites and has bestowed them upon us in a differentiated (polarized) state. Our evolutionary task is to integrate these opposites to a reconciled state. Our task at hand is one of tough love.

Kenneth

The Creator's Plan

Introduction

The Creator's plan is a hypothesis that outlines the Creator's vision for our space-time continuum. It attempts to consider the purpose for the creation of our Universe as presumably understood (space-time continuum), but it is extended to include the Creator's realm (fifth dimension). I have outlined a five-dimensional concept (a model) of the Universe along with an abstract model of the Creator.

The basic hypothesis for this plan is considered here from the perspective of my paper, "A Five-Dimensional Model of the Universe" (Copyright, May 17, 2007, TXU1-358-083) and my paper, "The Creator" (Copyright, December 9, 2008, TXU1-682-659).

The argument that the Creator is unknowable and can only be consciously activated through an individual, unconscious experience offers a reasonable view against knowing the Creator in any physical or psychic sense. However, our present limited understanding and perception of universal reality restricts and compromises any understanding of the Creator. Let us consider the models herein referred to and begin a new understanding of the Creator's presence.

A philosophy that ignores either the physical aspects or

the metaphysical laws of nature is a transient philosophy that will terminate because it ignores the Creator's plan for the Universe.

The physical and metaphysical components of the Creator's whole provide the energy components that created our space-time Universe and carry out the functional operation and governance of its entropic existence and its potential regeneration.

We begin the hypothesis of the Creator's plan with the assumption that the Creator is pre-existent to our space-time reality and is an eternal concept.

The Creator's plan is our universal nature — the fact of our reality. The purpose of this paper is to explore this sense of reality in the context of the Creator's plan.

There is always the Creator. Conceptually, the Creator pre-exists our sense of consciousness and resides in the fifth-dimensional realm displaced from our space-time continuum.

Our Perception of Reality

Our scientific community, as an operative discipline, primarily concerns itself with a sensate understanding of reality. The purpose of what we call science is to provide physical experiments that accurately and repeatably predict a process or an outcome. The services provided by this operative discipline have been extraordinary in their pursuit of understanding the physical aspects of our space-time continuum. This science is concerned with the experimental investigation and hypothetical explanation of natural phenomena and it essentially ignores any other class of phenomena. Our notion of science is primarily a physical engineering discipline. It does not concern itself with the concept of truth and, in that perspective, it does not concern itself with reality beyond a limited understanding of physical phenomena. The scientific community disdains the metaphysical aspects of reality but has, under occasional duress, reluctantly integrated into its body of work certain natural (metaphysical) laws that can no longer be ignored. The study of physics has historically been an empirical science. Its proof or verification has been understood from observation or experiment. Its contributions have relied upon practical experience without fundamental regard for theory. Essentially, empiricism relies on experience, primarily of the senses, as the only source of knowledge. In that perspective, empirical science (Newtonian physics) is primarily a sensate discipline. In a broader sense, the sensate describes only one of four cognitive functions/ types that also include intuition, thinking, and feeling.

As a practical matter, intuition, thinking, and to a lesser extent feeling have provided insights into the scientific knowledge "discovered" over the last centuries. However, their contributions have been ancillary to the primary focus of the empiricists and only grudgingly acknowledged or mostly misinterpreted when observations or experiments have indicated and suggested the "new quantum science" of reality. The empirical method will continue to defocus the "new quantum science" with results based on our limited model (space-time) of universal reality.

In its defense, empirical science and its attendant disciplines certainly must be regarded as western civilization's greatest contribution to our physical and industrial world. In no way can its past contributions be overstated. However, as we move closer to the atomic realm barrier (the fifth dimension), our sense of space-time reality will metamorphose to a new concept of reality. Newtonian physics slowly becomes less a science and more an engineering discipline that will certainly continue to provide practical answers to human physical needs and desires.

Empirical science and engineering will always be a partial answer (the sensate answer) to the scientific truths that will include intuition, thinking, and feeling. From these cognitive functions will come the ideas and the model for a new understanding of universal reality. This "new science" is in its infancy and it is called quantum physics in recognition of Max Planck's experiments on black bodies in 1900. My models presented here are based on the validity of quantum physics but not on the content of empirical absolutes.

The Possibility of Space-Time

Consider a concept of reality without our space-time continuum. The model would hypothesize the concept of the Creator's realm in an ether. The Creator's concept is in total harmony and perfect balance that constitutes the whole of reality. There is nothing else — the Creator's realm. All its power and glory manifest in its immeasurable physical energy along with its immutable natural laws. Unassailable and omnipotent — and everlasting.

From this realm, the Creator envisions an extension of its whole into what we perceive as our space-time continuum. The concept of matter is implicitly derived from the Creator's physical (mass) component in concert with the natural laws that are part of the Creator's metaphysical being. These energies that created our space-time continuum are derived from the whole of the Creator.

Our space-time continuum is an extension and implicit

derivative from the Creator's realm. The Creator's realm constitutes all existence, and the creation of our space-time continuum, by definition, is the only possible alternative to the extension of the Creator's realm. The Creator model implies that nothing physically or metaphysically exists that could suggest an alternative extension of reality. The Creator's realm, including our derived space-time continuum, is the whole of all reality — a five-dimensional reality.

The fact of our space-time continuum leads me to postulate that within the Creator's realm is the propensity to create and to re-create from its wholeness. The Creator does not recreate itself. The Creator is the whole of everything, and recreating itself is a contradiction in terms. It creates a new realm (space-time). A realm in violent turmoil, derived from the Creator's wholeness, into a spectrum of physical and metaphysical primordial soup.

It is the birth of possibilities — infinite possibilities in the context of finite time. The cognitive function latent in the concept of evolution (both physically and metaphysically) provides the way and the means toward a communion with the Creator.

The Creator's Universe can be none other than what it is. It contains the whole of the Creator's presence. Every aspect of the Creator's physical and metaphysical energy is present in some derivative/relational form or in some complex, cognitive function operating as natural laws within this universal (five-dimensional) construct.

The Creation of Space-Time

A question of whether the Creator's being conscious of itself would necessarily need conscious creatures is moot. Being conscious of itself would suggest an ego content, which is not part of the Creator's being. The Creator primarily functions as a systematic entity that rigorously follows universal natural laws. The models suggest that the Creator functions at a higher level of consciousness (beyond ego). The creation of space-time is not a random event or some senseless physical eruption, but a planned and orchestrated creation, by the Creator, with a purpose and a goal.

The Creator has set into motion the creation of our space-time continuum utilizing an indirect method (eco-system) employing countless species and creatures to carry out its evolutionary plan. Within the whole of this complex process — the intervening miracle of reflective ego-consciousness — the second cosmogony appears and takes form. The import of ego-consciousness is so fundamental to the whole process that its meaning is clouded within the cauldron of a seemingly senseless biological turmoil.

The result is the advent of our space-time continuum creation both physically and metaphysically. Finally, throughout a long biological process, ego-consciousness is found in the warm-blooded vertebrates possessed of a differentiated brain. This new consciousness in humans is sensed perhaps by design or groped for out of a complex, unconscious urge. Inherent in this evolutionary, differentiated ego-consciousness, the cognitive processes necessary to comprehend the Creator's meaning for its space-time creation now becomes a conditional prospect. And, in that perspective, the gift of cognition becomes human destiny.

The Creator's model contains an operational consciousness inherent in its dualistic nature. A fully reconciled consciousness that is without ego. A consciousness that pre-exists our space-time sense of reality and is integrated into the whole of the Creator's metaphysical component.

Max Planck's comment, "I regard matter as derivative from consciousness," is an extraordinary observation on the concept of consciousness. If matter is a derivative from consciousness, then it is a derivative of a higher level (beyond ego) of fifth-dimensional consciousness and is an implicit, dependent variable of that sense of consciousness. The consideration of the derivation of consciousness into matter is also an observation on a "new consciousness" introduced to our created space-time continuum. In effect, what we might perceive as the derived metaphysical consciousness from the Creator is, in fact, the new ego-consciousness that is a critical component to the Creator's plan. This is the advent of the second cosmology.

The Creator's metaphysical consciousness systematically operates the physical laws that will introduce matter into our space-time continuum as a derivative of fifth-dimensional mass. This derivative process is the primary action that creates, in a physical sense, our space-time continuum. It is the advent of the first cosmology. The Creator utilizes its fundamental physical and metaphysical components to create our space-time continuum from its eternal and conceptual whole.

The Creator's Plan

Our space-time continuum is an implicit derivative from the Creator's whole, and it is the consequence of the Creator's direct intent to introduce our space-time continuum into a broader perspective of universal reality. The catalyst for the creation of space-time is the eternal, universal calculus. The calculus is a metaphysical natural law inherent in the Creator's whole. The calculus and its derivations fundamentally represent variation with respect to change, in conditions or perspective. Potentially, it is a transition from one state to another. It requires a transfer of physical and metaphysical energy to give birth to a new reality (space-time). The trauma of change, its primordial consequences and turmoil, represent the conditions for the complex emergence of what we call space and time.

The question is posited as to whether our space-time continuum is an integral part of the Creator's plan, or is it simply an arbitrary circumstance from a mindless physical event? Arbitrary conditions for the creation of space-time could not be supported by the Creator model. The Creator is the whole of all existence and of all power and energy. This perspective leads to an ordained or pre-determined condition for the creation of our space-time reality.

The Creator's complex nature is the basis for my hypothesis that attempts to understand the Creator's plan and its purpose for our space-time creation.

The natural laws of the Universe (metaphysical) are inextricably linked to the physical (mass-motion) energy of the Creator. These two entities characterize the intrinsic nature of the Creator. The Creator's nature is sustained by a totally efficient process through which it abides in that nature. The Creator operates as a whole functional system. The whole system is all of its focus and its energy.

The Creator's realm (fifth dimension) has been defined by my model. The metaphysical laws that govern the whole of reality (the five-dimensional Universe) is the equivalent (the analog) of the physical concept of motion, of change, of growth, and of evolution. The proposition is offered, in effect, that the natural laws inherent in the the Creator's whole are fundamental to the implicit urgency of creation. Specifically, in this case, our space-time continuum creation. This process is understood to be directly related to the concept of implicit differentiation.

1. The Opposites

The attempt to connect the idea of the Creator's plan to the urgency for the creation of our space-time continuum rests upon the validity of the Creator's model, particularly in relation to natural laws. These natural laws are represented in part by the nature of the opposites that are at the core of the Creator's whole.

The opposites are a reconciled, integrated entity within the model of the Creator's whole. The opposites function as to the laws of their conceptual ideation. The opposites are the fundamental component of the metaphysical process of creation and are directly inter/intra-operational with the physical mass-motion component of the Creator's whole. In contrast, unreconciled opposites are diffused, inefficient, and incoherent products dissociated by the derivative process of the Creator's plan for our space-time continuum. In this evolutionary process, the opposites have become unreconciled from the Creator's integrated, reconciled center (fifth-dimensional) toward a dissipated polar abyss. It is the condition that we observe as our sense of reality in our space-time continuum.

The opposites are introduced (derived) to us in an undifferentiated mode from the Creator. This condition implies that the opposites (pre-existent to ego-consciousness) in a new dimensional mode (space-time) represent the building blocks of universal cognition and the truth latent in its metaphysical properties and energy. The opposites in space-time represent the change from the Creator's metaphysical whole to the sum of all its incremental (infinitesimal) variations in a new paradigm. This metaphysical derivation of the opposites represents our cognitive reality and determines our metaphysical relationship to the Creator — always cognizant that we are dimensionally displaced from the Creator's realm. This new paradigm of derived undifferentiated opposites provides the process through which we find our path toward metaphysical understanding and truth. The reconciliation of the opposites (differentiated) is a fifth-dimensional concept. Its metaphysical energy and its attendant governance of the natural laws are not directly translatable to our space-time creation. In effect, we do not marshal metaphysical energy through understanding, i.e., we do not become the Creator. We simply begin the process of understanding the nature of our Universe and, by extension, the nature of the Creator.

This process will lead us away from ego-consciousness toward a higher consciousness that could provide – through the calculus of integration – a higher state of metaphysical perception and potential metaphysical energy.

Assuming you are able to reconcile the opposites from an ego-conscious perspective, then you have transcended the ego from our space-time level of consciousness. In that evolutionary sense, you are beginning to relate to the Creator's level of consciousness with all its attendant truth and power.

Again, the Creator has presented the opposites to us (space-time) in an undifferentiated mode. For example, the opposites of good-evil are presented as polar entities. Evil is defined as morally bad or wrong, wicked, causing ruin, injury, or pain, harmful. In an undifferentiated sense, that definition is certainly our sentient perception of the concept of evil. However, the concept of the opposites pre-exists ego-consciousness and represents the metaphysical side of the Creator's whole. In this sense, good-evil function in a differentiated mode (reconciled) and without ego-consciousness. In this state of higher consciousness, the opposites (good-evil) could be represented as ageless, archetypal images. In another sense, they might be seen as a spectrum of infinite facets and possibilities. In either sense, to confront the full image/spectrum of this pair of opposites (good-evil) would be a revelation.

2. Evolution

Motion is the fundamental universal (five dimensional) constant. The Universe, in any sentient, living sense, is not possible without motion. Evolution, and its aspect of change, is a form of motion involving both physical and metaphysical components. This concept is derived from the essence of the Creator's presence, and to us by fate ordained, as physical and metaphysical natural laws. Time is a dimensional, directional aspect of our reality derived from motion that leads us toward a conclusion — a goal. A goal of time is our cognitive process through evolution. The history of time is our evolution.

Our vision of reality is primarily a study in evolution. The images and projections of our material world (both physical and metaphysical), the nature of reality, represent the Creator's plan for our collective humanity and directs its progression toward our final evolution.

The concept of evolution is rooted in the natural laws of the Creator (pre-exists ego-consciousness). It is conceptually metaphysical and is implicit in its derivation (introduced into space-time). Evolution is a gift from the Creator's whole, just as the calculus, the complex functions of relativity, and ego-consciousness are gifts from the Creator.

The fundamental purpose of any life system is to evolve. Its evolutionary path, whether physical or metaphysical, is not only in service of its survival and that of its issue, but towards its own and its individual potential. The process is to develop its unique perfection relative to the Creator's plan.

Our task is to evolve both physically and metaphysically. In our present physical form (matter), we cannot enter the Creator's realm. Our living physical role in the Creator's plan is limited by time and dimension. However, we are the essence of the Creator's whole and that essence which the Creator endowed. While our essence will modify and change its form and function, it will be sustained throughout the life cycle of our universal system.

There is a metaphysical connection between our space-time reality and the Creator's realm. A critical component of evolution, understood metaphysically, is to relate our progress in the reconciliation of the opposites with the Creator's metaphysical perfection. This is our worldly chore, our goal, our attainment. The condition where the Creator codifies our ego-conscious progress in relation to its supreme consciousness (fifth dimension).

Humankind, in any physical or metaphysical sense, does not become one with the Creator. We are not conscious of the Creator's realm and have no material connection to that "existence." All our connection with the Creator's realm has been derived for us from the Creator's whole. All our understanding of the Creator is a perception based on our space-time reality as introduced by the Creator through the derivation of matter and all its natural laws. We are the recipients of these gifts of life and we are the legacy by which we seek to understand the aura of the Creator's presence.

In the cauldron of the evolutionary process, the Creator's plan offers the road to a higher consciousness (away from ego-consciousness) and is the road away from turmoil and chaos. It is toward a path that defines the Creator's essence within us as we identify that essence within our complete selves. In the final analysis, this evolutionary path could potentially surpass the ego function.

Our destiny is to evolve. It is the primary function of living creatures to evolve. This evolutionary concept allows a further understanding and reconciling of those gifts of life from the Creator to become one with the unity of our existence and our natural laws. These gifts from the Creator are signposts to recognize our fifth-dimension connection to the Creator. In life, we have no direct connection to the Creator. We are dimensionally separate but inextricably linked to the Creator's realm. The Creator's realm is omnipresent in our being.

3. Relativity

Relativity is generally understood as a quasi-physical phenomenon whereby the dimensions in our space-time continuum undergo changes (elasticity) dependent on variations in input conditions. However, relativity in a philosophical sense is also defined as existence dependent solely upon relation to a thinking mind. A state of dependence exists when the existence or significance of one entity is dependent upon that of another. In fact, relativity is seen as both a physical and a metaphysical entity and is pervasive in nature. In a physical sense, relativity means any behavioral phenomenon or system subject to variances in input conditions. In a broader, metaphysical sense, relativity is a concept innate in the Creator's natural laws that command dependent significance of one entity to another.

Relativity is pervasive in the nature of the Universe. The Creator's nature suggests that all things are related and inter/intra-connected. All things physical and metaphysical belong in a complex process that makes up our Universe (five-dimensional reality). We are the cognitive recipients of this natural phenomenon called relativity, which is a beacon toward cognitive understanding and truth.

The concept of relativity has been provided to us by the Creator as a consequence of its natural laws. In a physical sense, relativity provides us with an opportunity to understand the critical inter/intra-workings of nature which include the phenomena of the dependence of eco-systems and the behavioral patterns of space-time under varying conditions. In a metaphysical sense, relativity is a universal entity offered from the essence of the Creator's whole. It comes to us as a first principle of nature. In this sense, relativity represents the nature of the interaction among all living things.

From this concept, the Creator puts into action the link between its higher consciousness and our long journey of understanding the nature of things through the lens of ego-consciousness.

4. Inferences from the Plan

The Creator's plan for our space-time continuum has introduced the concepts of the opposites, evolution, and relativity. My models have hypothesized these concepts as both physical and metaphysical entities. These concepts come to us as first principles from the Creator's whole and are omnipresent. They pre-exist ego-consciousness and belong to a realm of higher consciousness. They are not the sole possession of earth or our solar system, but rather are universal constructs from the ubiquitous essence of the Creator. They provide the guideposts to a higher consciousness and the beacons toward the light of understanding and truth. They come to us as a gift and as a challenge to the capacity of our perception – and to a closer interrelationship with the aura of the Creator.

Comments on The Creator's Plan

1. A question is advanced as to whether death is the ultimate end or a doorway. The models imply that the essence of cognition (the second cosmology) will persist throughout the history of our galactic time period. Humanity's contribution to the focus of that cognitive meaning (the Creator's goal) will be modulated (will be written) on the wave pulses of time. This collective cognition contribution will represent the history of humankind's metaphysical progress (its evolution) as a chorus of all our collective, yet individual, inputs. In this sense (a metaphysical sense), the individual will exist throughout all recorded galactic time.

In a physical sense, the human's dead body (its container) — the dust of physical being — is consumed as to its individual function and purpose. The remains belong to the physical world and their particular place in the scheme of the physical Universe. The remains lose their identity as a specific human entity, but leave an imprint as part of each individual's uniqueness. In an absolute five-dimensional sense, nothing ever dies.

2. Our solar system and our galaxy are finite entities and will die their natural death. They will be regenerated into "new worlds" and new galaxies. Time (a derivative of motion) will begin again and the Creator's plan will follow its inexorable evolutionary path.

3. We are, and in many respects will always be, creatures of our planet and our simple solar system. Yet, we are fundamentally creatures of our galaxy and of the entire Universe. We are a part of the Creator's plan and of the Creator itself. Our essence is manifested from the Creator's fundamental whole. This is our blessing and this is our gift. The natural laws, in combination with the Creator's physical and metaphysical energy, dictate our reality — any reality. They are the Creator's cognitive reality, and through the process of implicit derivation, our space-time reality.

4. The models require that the physical and metaphysical components of the Creator's presence be manifest in the existence of universal reality seen as a five-dimensional construct. However, if we were to assume that all of universal reality is simply our space-time continuum (four-dimensional), then the Creator of that reality must be a conscious presence in that reality. Consequently, the Creator would be within our immediate grasp. The Creator would then become an entity in the study of matter. In that context, the Creator could not be other than matter and would be vulnerable to its creation. This concept of Creator/Universe would be its own final absurdity.

5. Cognizance is part of the Creator's plan for us to explore the content and extent of our reality. The nature of cognizance is a metaphysical entity within the Creator's realm. For humankind, cognizance was introduced in the form of ego-consciousness. For us, consciousness ordinarily functions in a relative sense with its precepts and attitudes conditioned by changing levels of understanding and experience. Our history shows that levels of understanding are perceived and honed on the pumice stones of life as a socially collective, interactive process.

Correspondence on The Creator's Plan with Larry Staples, Ph.D., Jungian Analyst

Ken,

With the keen passion and deep commitment you have for your ideas, I'm not at all surprised that a preacher and/or teacher calling beckons you from time to time. In a way, you are faced with a marketing problem in the highest and best sense of the word. What is the optimal way to get a message to the people one wishes to reach? Fortunately, today, you don't have to have a church to do it. Your pulpit can be the internet that casts a net far beyond a local parish. All spiritual leaders become iconoclasts. It can be dangerous work that is also richly fulfilling.

I was touched by your statement about "these abstract concepts that almost haunt me." It occurred to me that since God is the most abstract entity we can imagine, we may need in our lives to become increasingly abstract, if we are to encounter her/him. Maybe that partly explains your embrace of the abstract in your reflections about the Creator. It can feel awfully lonely, if along the way you don't encounter others striving for similar levels of abstraction. Don't despair. I know they are out there.

Larry

Larry,

Thank you for your time and your honest and straightforward response to my paper. It means a good deal to me that you prioritized your energies in my behalf.

Sometimes I feel that my role in life is to be an iconoclast — someone has to do the dirty work, yet I cannot escape these abstract concepts that almost haunt me. The call of the teacher or pastor is sometimes present, but I feel too lazy or ill-equipped to wear that cloth.

Indeed, your comments are well taken on the abstract nature of the material, coupled with the fundamental need to relate these concepts to the three disciplines (physics, psychology, philosophy). In fact, this was the root of the challenge that almost dissuaded me from the task of writing the papers. It is extremely frustrating to discuss metaphysical concepts with a physicist when the response is a closing curtain or a curt comment. In this vein, it was necessary to have a plan (engineering discipline) to begin the process using "basic models." The three papers represent those models — the road map of a hypothesis. The models/plan are only the "bones" of the hypothesis that I hope will better explain the functioning and operation of the Creator's Universe. I hope the models will be the catalyst for me (and perhaps others) to put some meat on the bones.

Your idea about my creating a blog is just exactly what I'm thinking of doing. I'm already working on a few ideas that will attempt to explain/discuss certain aspects of the models similar to the question in "The Creator's Plan" about whether death is the ultimate end or a doorway. There is no one answer. The models hypothesize that any fundamental truth must contain both a physical and a metaphysical component.

When you ask for examples of the scientific community relying on experimental or practical experience without fundamental regard to theory, my response is that the scientific community disdains theory. Our present "science" is empirically driven and primarily considers only repeatable experimental or practical results — not systematically organized knowledge. I am trying with my models to assault the bastions of the "science."

The Creator's Plan is a hypothesis (otherwise it would be an extraordinary inflation) and yet my conception of the Creator's Plan is an intuitive construct in an abstract sense.

Kenneth

Correspondence on The Creator's Plan with Peter Kearney, former Priest

Kenneth,

I misunderstood your thought about the Creator as a non-personal entity. I remain struck by your clear affirmation of the Creator as having a physical component, if one may say "component" about such a Being. A further question in that area that occurs to me now is whether we have to have a "creator" at all.

Peter

Peter,

I want to focus on your comment about the Creator as a non-personal entity. The hypothesis would not support that conclusion. Our space-time sense of reality is a derivative of the Creator's whole. Our reality contains all the essences of the Creator. Every aspect of the Creator's physical and non-physical entities are present in us in some derivative/relative form or in some complex cognitive function operating as natural laws within our complete universal (five-dimensional) construct. The Creator embraces all of life with its presence on any physical or metaphysical level — and for us (humankind) on a cognitive level. We individually will always be a personal part of the Creator throughout all of measured time.

Our limited investigations into the "subatomic world" have been reported from a space-time (four-dimensional) perspective (empirical science). We can interpret fifth-dimensional data — let's say from Bohr's model of the atom, which is a hypothesis — but we cannot actually see fifth-dimensional products. The ability to see mass will always be an interpretation of a fifth-dimensional product based on some hypothetical model. The laws of nature — according to my models — are immutable. They represent the essences of the metaphysical component of the Creator and are universal constants.

I am speaking in the language of science because that is my primary discipline. It is also an important language because the Creator is a complex entity with a powerful physical presence. Also, the models are better presented in this language. Even more important, the world of science is deeply rooted in Aristotelian ideas about the senses as the only source of knowledge. However, it is impossible to proceed toward any level of truth and understanding with this limited perspective. If my models cannot integrate the history of extraordinary ideas and concepts from philosophy, psychology, religion, and science (on one level seen as one concept), then my work will have been in vain to all except me.

Kenneth

Correspondence on the Creator's Plan with Norman Theiss, Lutheran Pastor

Kenneth,

From your paper "The Creator's Plan" your description that we are part of the Creator's plan and of the Creator itself. Our essence is manifest from the Creator's fundamental whole. This is our blessing and this is our gift. These are profound and powerful thoughts. Are you saying that we are partners in the Creator's plan, that is, partners with the Creator? Is our essence a manifestation of the Creator's whole? If this is a blessing, then did the Creator give the blessing? If this is a gift, did the Creator give the gift? Is not blessing or giving a gift a conscious act done with intention? If we are the recipients of this blessing and this gift, are we not in the presence of benign creative intention?

This too is anthropomorphism. We are projecting onto a Creator our need to believe that we exist, that we have a Creator who blesses us and gives us our role in nature. But the fact is that we do think we exist and we do need to know who we are. Why? Does the fact that we project One who knows and cares about us mean that there could not be such a One?

Norm

Norm,

No! We are not partners with the Creator. We are the clay of the Creator's plan. Philosophically, my core belief (the *sine qua non*) is that there must be a fundamental essence (an element) that relates the creation process to the created. That essence is a manifestation of the Creator's whole. Is it a blessing or a gift? I would prefer to say it is a complex plan designed by the Creator. We are the objects of this plan. We are its recipients.

I do not see a Creator who blesses us and gives us our role in nature. I see this creative process as an evolutionary experiment that is rife with pitfalls and dangers. However, not so much in an ecological sense as in a cognitive ego sense. If I am projecting onto the Creator my need to believe that we exist — my first task is to withdraw that projection.

I would not argue that projection is a critical dynamic in human society. It is a manifestation of ego consciousness. It is a dynamic that needs to be understood and assimilated into a higher consciousness.

Kenneth

A Quantum Perspective On Life After Death

Introduction

In a western scientific sense, we live in a created, empirical world. Life and death conditions in this created world logically follow the ordained pattern of our cyclical, generational posterity. Also, we are creatures of an entropic, temporal environment. Our scientific ideas about life and death are generally related to the practical (sensate) perspective that recognizes its inevitable demise.

In a religious and philosophical sense, our ideas about life and death are suggested by revelation, mythology, and mysticism. Generally speaking, there is little experimental evidence either related to or directly connected to our physical, created world. Our path to understanding life and death issues becomes a speculative process since we have no apparent connection to an afterlife. This problematical situation is compounded by the human tendency to favor and support particular ingrained belief systems.

The question of any possible life after death perspective becomes an almost impossible morass of confusion, special interests, and biases. Unless the question of life after death is based on repeatable natural functions and operational data in the creation process (ordained by the Creator), the question is limited to an exercise in religious and philosophical projections.

In this paper, I intend to explore the possibility of any forms of human life after death from data traces in the natural creation process focused on a quantum hypothesis of universal reality.

Organizing Life and Death Ideas in a Quantum World

It is not theoretically feasible to understand fully the concept/idea of human life after death in a created, empirical world — a world that is scientifically considered to be the whole of reality. At issue is that while the empirical world can theoretically be understood, the Creator's realm (the creation system) remains a complex mystery.

It is not unreasonable to assume that this "Creator's realm" will always be a mystery — a realm beyond our empirical reach, and a place that defies recognition and cognition. However, this situation has merit particularly if we were simply endowed by the Creator with a cognitive capacity that is limited to a strict sentient/empirical perspective. To paraphrase the words of T.E. Lawrence: "The living knew themselves just sentient puppets on the Creator's stage."

However, the theoretical possibility of understanding a reality beyond the empirical has been suggested by the advent of the quantum era. The resultant quantum data base for an expanded (beyond space-time) reality suggests that the present cognitive capacity of the empirical mind has potentially been opened to a new perspective.

This new perspective peeks at us from nature's behavior patterns. It announces its perspective from uncertainty principles and complementarity to incidents of quantum entanglement. It is reflected in the extraordinary immutable natural laws of thermodynamics and the calculus. We are dealing here with nature's patterns beyond the physical limitations of our created empirical world. In a sense, we are experiencing the energy that created our empirical world. This eternal energy — both physical and metaphysical — represents our data connection to the creation process. It represents our link to the Creator, and it is our connecting essence in the creation process.

The Gift of Life

In the process of creation, the Creator provided the gift of life to us as a physical container we refer to as the body. In that physical sense, we are mortal. Our bodies are a container of entropic matter in which the process of decay begins at inception — birth to death. Death is the natural consequence of living in our created empirical world.

In conjunction with the gift of life, the Creator provided us with a natural, generational process operating through the auspices of a living DNA/RNA component. This generational component specifically allows us the necessary time factor for our evolution before our created ecological platform (the solar system) dies its own natural death. Further, by definition, the created cannot create. The DNA/RNA component (noting evolutionary modifications) is not a creative activity, but as noted a generational concept. In our created, empirical sense of reality (physical), the question of life after death (ignoring any medical/legal definitions of death) for any living species would be an entropic impossibility defying the laws of nature.

However, there remains a nagging issue for the efficacy of any physical possibility of life after death. When we speak of our created world, the physical structure of that world is described as matter. Also, within the physical structure of our being, a related energy entity we call mass is present. However, mass is an eternal entity that functionally operates in a related, but different, dimension. (See my paper "A Five-Dimensional Model of the Universe.") At the time of physical death, mass energy relinquishes its functional purpose from matter toward a process of decay. We become the dust of our ancestors.

Extending the premise of life after physical death, can our created matter can be reconstituted (integrated) into mass, the eternal entity? Matter would have to be re-created into something alien to its creation to continue beyond its life cycle. While matter is intricately related to mass, it is functionally and dimensionally separate. As a consequence. matter is not an entity capable of operating in an eternal system. The death of living matter is a natural consequence of the gift of life.

In a physcial sense, if the body could retain its related mass energy component, which is eternal, then that connective, created relationship could potentially persist in a cycle beyond death. Hypothetically, ending the physical matter connection at death from our created process would require a new mass-induced life cycle toward a condition beyond its normal physical process. However, that condition presupposes that the gift of life is an eternal offering. In that event, the mass energy of life in the physical body would forever remain in its functional physical form. Then, at death, we become immortal.

But mass has no function in an decaying process (matter), and matter has no function or purpose in an eternal system. At death, the bodily structure (matter) loses form and degenerates to its core components (elements, molecules) toward a return to its DNA/RNA in a cycle of physical death. Matter will always be matter, and its related mass energy will cease.

The mass quotient of energy present in the physical process of living matter cannot be sustained in the death of living matter. It would be an unnatural condition. Life after death of entropic matter can only be sustained by a transfer of eternal mass energy to a condition of metaphysically-related functions. In this case, it would require a cognitive energy transfer.

What is the meaning of death? What happens when we "shuffle off this mortal coil"? Physical matter obeys the laws of entropy and ceases its existence. As stated, the physical body returns to the dust of the ecosystem that nourished it. Is that all of what we are — a physical entity, a flesh and blood container?

We are also a sentient species endowed with the gift of cognition. The cognitive process is not a physical entity. It is a natural metaphysical entity. It then becomes necessary to consider our personal relationship with the gift of cognition and the fact that we are dealing with metaphysical properties of a natural, universal system. Nature provides its empirical "patterns" of the immutable laws that govern our created world and, by extension, operates its complex physical and metaphysical world. The Universe operates as a functionally natural system.

At this point, it is necessary to link our physical body to the Creator's second gift to us — the gift of cognition. The question is whether our physical body is forever connected to a cognitive entity and whether that entity — inextricably linked — could transcend the body's physical lifetime cycle, or if it expires along with the physical body at death. The gift of physical life in relation to the gift of cognition suggests a natural connection of our creation to the aura of the Creator. In this sense, we embody the aura of the Creator's whole. We are part of the natural process of the whole of the Universe — beyond our empirical creation.

The Gift of Cognition

The dictionary definition of cognition is the mental process or faculty by which knowledge is acquired, the range of what can be known or understood.

The Creator endowed us with two precious gifts. In addition to the gift of physical life, we have been blessed with the extraordinary gift of cognition. Cognition cannot be understood as a physical entity; rather it embodies the laws of nature. By extension, it is not a temporal, entropic concept. Cognition belongs to the nature of an eternal system. It represents the essence of the Creator's nature which is bequeathed to us in a nascent undifferentiated form (ego-consciousness). Hypothetically, this gift is given to us with a sense of evolutionary responsibility aimed toward reaching a differentiated level of higher consciousness, beyond the ego.

Correspondence on Life After Death with Peter Kearney, former Catholic Priest

Kenneth,

In the Introduction, you state that we have no apparent connection to an afterlife. For myself, I wonder should we give more consideration to those who tell of near-death experiences. Clare and I recently read one book, Raymond

Moody's Life after Life. I was a little surprised at how critical he was, and yet he was willing to accept the idea that these experiences were not just hallucinatory.

In the section Gift of Life, the last paragraph was very difficult, especially your reference to the aura of the Creator, but, as I expected, you gave it a fuller treatment in what followed. One key sentence was: Cognition belongs to the nature of an eternal system. Also, you affirmed that cognition permeates the whole of reality. For myself, I would see not cognition but knowability as permeating all reality. What you assert as cognition I see rather as being. Cognition is the activity of a knower, based on being or the knowability of all things. But knowability is a potency that demands a knower. I suppose the Creator would be the knower of all things. Perhaps I misunderstand, but it seems that you have taken the activity of a knower (cognition) and projected that on to all created reality. Or is this just a quibbling over words on my part?

The last sentence in the section Gift of Cognition includes the clause: we are as immortal as time itself. It seems odd to me to be back in the world of time when we seemed to be in the midst of eternity. Will time be immortal?

Peter

Peter,

Thank you for reading my paper on life after death and reporting your comments.

My reference to the fact that we have no apparent connection to an afterlife means only the dictionary definition of apparent — "readily understood or perceived, plain or obvious." Near death experiences are not plain or obvious. They are personal and complicated psychological responses to traumatic experiences. I don't discount these heartfelt reactions.

Regarding cognition as belonging to the nature of an eternal system, I included the definition of cognition because of potential misunderstanding of the term. Cognition is defined as the mental processes or faculty by which knowledge is acquired, the range of what can be known or understood. The definition is all-inclusive. It does not limit or specify a subset of a particular knowability nor does it morph into a definition of "being." Yes, cognition demands a "knower" and that "knower" is the Creator. Cognition is an eternal, natural law and it is a gift to us from the Creator. The question is whether this gift of cognition is simply limited to our created empirical world or whether we are ordained with potential access to the whole of its spectrum.

Related to the gift of cognition, my comment that we are as immortal as time itself was offered as a poetic attempt to support my hypothetical contention that there remains a potential cognitive life after death. To be exact, my models contend that our space-time system was created and that time is a temporal entity (derived from motion). Time will last for as long as our created world and all of its past and future generations exist. Time is only part of an eternal system in a poetic sense, but any claim of its immortality is relational to the lifetime of our created, entropic world. It staggers the imagination to contemplate the end of time and the end of our created world.

Peter, stay with me on this! The crux of my hypothesis (eternal life after death) rests on the assumption of whether the gift of cognition is limited to our empirical world or whether it is potentially available to us with the totality of its eternal spectrum. Hypothetically, if we contain the seeds of the Creator's eternal cognition then, by definition, we are in a metaphysical sense immortal. QED! However, if the extent of our gift of cognition is limited to our empirical creation, then the potential for any life after death is constrained by the limits of our entropic creation — the limits of time. An answer to this question is presently only hypothetical.

Kenneth

Correspondence on Life After Death with Larry Partain, Ph.D. Physicist, Translational Research Associates

Ken,

I am always quite stimulated by your blogs. They seem to catch my attention and demand that I start thinking in some alternative way. This applies to your latest blog on life after death from a quantum perspective. In general I tend not to accept life after death except in a couple of very limited ways. I tend to see nothing in nature that would give life after death only to humans and not other animals. And that seems unreasonable to me. The first exception is DNA that both animals and plants have that passes on to their descendants all the improvements that come from "survival of the fittest." The second is a written language that sets humans apart in passing on hard-gained knowledge so that new scientists and engineers can "stand on the shoulders of giants." However, neither of these are what Biblical descriptions mean by going to heaven or hell upon death and/or rising from the dead.

In considering energy and mass, since Einstein's $E = mc^2$, I tend to think of them as two aspects of the same whole. As

I understand "big bang" theory, the Universe started with just energy. A relatively short time after this start, quarks started to form that produced protons (two up and one down quark) and neutrons (one up and two down quarks). Protons and neutrons do have mass that came from converting original energy into mass. I am not sure about electrons that do have mass. A little time later there was an ionized plasma of electrons, protons, and neutrons until the expansion lowered energy density enough so that electrons, protons, and neutrons could form into charge-neutral atoms, starting with hydrogen. The resulting stars combined these two atoms all the way up to carbon. For atoms larger than that, super nova explosions were required.

One important thing you directly address is "cognition." To me this is indeed a gift that apparently only humans have that allowed advanced civilizations to form simultaneously all about the world (3,000 to 5,000 years ago). To me, the giver of this special "cognition" is an active intelligence that not only accounts for all of science and its major advances, but also participates in the Universe over long term to make the very rare conditions that allow humans to develop and thrive. By this I mean a very long term active and enduring intelligence's participation in generating Universe conditions where humans can continue, at least until the next (or 6th) mass extinction when 75% of all advanced animal life on earth becomes extinct. The latter is what I associate with your fifth dimension of the Universe that I find so appealing.

Larry

Larry,

Thank you for your response to my paper on life after death. I apologize for my late response.

I was particularly impressed with your comment on the nature of all animals being afforded life after death. This idea should be a paper in itself, but my particular focus was related to a limited cognitive process in humans. I have struggled with your reference to all creatures and the whole spectrum of physical life. You have given me the energy to try again.

Larry, it will always be that scientists and engineers stand on what came before them — and what they understood of it. It is folly to think that all of knowledge belongs to the individual — it belongs to our collective humanity.

Certainly there is a relationship between energy and mass, and if you ignore a complicated relativistic kinetic energy factor (a particle factor) conveniently removed from the equation by assuming the speed of relativistic particles to be zero, then, yes, $E=mc^2$. Einstein knew the equation to be approximate, but it is operational in our empirical world.

Yes, the giver of cognition is an active intelligence in our created world. On this perspective, we wholly agree. And so too is our extraordinary ecosystem provided as a stage for the development of our nascent cognition and our evolution.

Kenneth

Correspondence on Life After Death with Larry Staples, Ph.D., Jungian Analyst

Kenneth,

I've read with interest your paper on the subject of life after death. You certainly offer some novel ideas. As in the case of past readings of your material, I am often stumped by my own shortcoming with respect to scientific knowledge. I certainly agree that discussions of life after death must in the end be based on speculations for which there is no empirical proof. As far as we know, no one has ever been there and come back to tell about it. Like you, I can easily imagine life after death, if I assume that death represents some kind of transformation of this life and matter into some other form.

It does seem to me that your writings about life after death are consistent with your other papers about the fifth dimension. I am aware of some poetic and philosophic ideas about this subject that seem in some ways to parallel your concepts. For example, T.S. Eliot, in his poem "Four Quartets" (Little Gidding) writes:

And the end of all our exploring Will be to arrive at the place where we started And know it for the first time.

I suspect his "place where we started" bears some semblance to your fifth dimension. And to know a place for the first time suggests the existence of a development of a level of consciousness that did not exist when we were first created. We were created with the potential for cognition and consciousness, but the potential was as yet undeveloped.

Plato in his allegory of the cave also suggests the existence of a realm that bears some similarity to your fifth dimension. The cave is a location of eternal forms of which all of manifest life is a reflection. I suspect he is describing in philosophical terms a realm that has some similarity to your fifth dimension, expressed in more scientific terms.

Larry

Larry,

Thank you for reading my paper on the potential for life after death.

Yes, life after death speculations are limited by the absence of any empirical proof. Unfortunately this will always be the case in reference to created matter since it is entropic by nature. Dust be my physical destiny (pardon the paraphrase). The dilemma becomes complicated by introducing mass (an eternal entity) into a cauldron of understanding beyond the empirical. Science confuses the issue by casually referring to matter (entropic) and mass (eternal) as "big" and "small." By nature, while these entities are intimately related, they are dimensionally and functionally displaced. My hypothetical prospect of some form of transformation (life after death) is related to our gift of cognition which by definition operates as a metaphysical process.

Yes, we are created with the potential for cognition, but the potential was as yet undeveloped. Shall we call this condition an evolutionary journey to consciousness and understanding. A process leading toward a higher level of consciousness (beyond the ego) toward an explanation of the purpose for which we were created.

Kenneth

Cognition

If the gift of cognition to humankind is an eternal concept
What is our relationship to that gift and to the eternal
    principles of its offering?
Why were we ordained for the selected offering of this gift?
What an extraordinary gift
What a humbling responsibility
Not only to ourselves, but to any sense of cognitive
    projection (beyond ego)
To a welcome place
To an eternal welcoming place

Not of the body, but of the soul
We are but a ghostly image of what is construed as whole
A created image of what is ordained or possible
And we carry this offering as a yoke
As a trial, to a place we can never know and only assume
That cognitive traits somehow persist, throughout all time,
To an eternal welcoming place.

A Prayer

Creator, I pray for the wisdom to understand the aura of
  your presence
I have floundered with a host of Gods
In a sea of images and projections
Help me to understand the meaning in our lives
The purpose we serve to humankind and unto our Creator.

Teach me virtues from their abundant offerings
And lead me onto the path of life's purpose
Give me the strength to discipline myself to the trials of life
And walk with me in the shadows of fear and despair.

I have witnessed the rapture of love
It is the foundation upon which all of your temples have
  risen
I seek to live that that love all the days of my life — here
  on earth —
And wherever life treads through eternity with you.

Epilogue

(with appreciation to Hillel)

If I am not for myself, who shall be for me?

If I am only for myself, what am I?

If I question, I may discover myself.

If not now, when?

Made in the USA
Columbia, SC
14 July 2020

13069165R00127